Béla Schick and the World of Children

Books by Antoni Gronowicz

BOLEK

CHOPIN

PADEREWSKI

TCHAIKOVSKY

RACHMANINOFF

HITLER'S WIFE

FOUR FROM THE OLD TOWN

THE PIASTS OF POLAND

GALLANT GENERAL

PATTERN FOR PEACE

BÉLA SCHICK AND THE WORLD OF CHILDREN

Most recent picture of Dr. and Mrs. Béla Schick with their dog, Mickey

Antoni Gronowicz

BÉLA SCHICK
AND THE WORLD
OF CHILDREN

WITH THIRTY-TWO PAGES

OF ILLUSTRATIONS

Abelard-Schuman, New York

Printed and bound in the United States of America
Published simultaneously in Canada by Nelson, Foster & Scott, Ltd.

To

CATHARINE FRIES SCHICK

Contents

Preface

BY RENÉ J. DUBOS

The Rockefeller Institute for Medical Research, New York City

To HIS COUNTLESS FRIENDS THROUGHOUT THE WORLD, THE HERO OF this book is known as a very lovable human being, endowed with much vigor, tempered by gentle smiling wisdom. The medical profession acknowledges him as the dean of pediatricians, and as one of the pioneers in the scientific study of allergic and immunological phenomena. Yet, to hundreds of millions of other men over the whole planet, the name Schick calls to mind not a person, but merely a scratch on the arm performed to test susceptibility to diphtheria. Like Volta, Pasteur, and a few other scientists whose contributions affect our everyday life, Béla Schick must resign himself to seeing his name reduced—or is it not rather magnified—to the size of a common household word, one of almost universal usage. Indeed, the *Schick test* is as much a part of modern life as is the measurement of *voltage*, or the *pasteurization* of foodstuffs. The ancients made gods of those whom they wanted to honor. More prosaically, we convert into common language the names of the great servants of our society.

There is much interest and entertainment for everyone in Mr. Gronowicz's captivating story. It puts on record and describes with their historical settings in Europe and in this country, Dr. Schick's many contributions to medicine, particularly in the world of children. By the pleasant artifice of vivid anecdotes—all in the true spirit of their hero—Mr. Gronowicz evokes the debonair charm that Dr. Schick has manifested in all phases of his life—be it as the private citizen moving unobtrusively among his fellow men and bringing good cheer to all, the devoted physician to whom so many are indebted, or the scientist who pioneered in several fields of medical research. Furthermore, there are lessons also to be read in the pages of this book—not only lessons of quiet courage and genial common sense, but also a philosophy for those dedicated to the pursuit of biological sciences.

It is somewhat startling, and very reassuring, to realize that most of the fundamental knowledge of allergy was worked out half a century ago by two young physicians still in their twenties, working in Vienna with primitive equipment and little help, but rich in enthusiasm and imagination. In the years that have elapsed since their original work, hundreds of highly trained investigators, helped by skilled technicians and using complicated apparatus, have done little more than gild the lily that first blossomed forth in 1905, in the form of the classical book by von Pirquet and Schick, *Die Serumkrankheit*.

It is an unusual and inspiring experience to follow Béla Schick, pursuing the practical consequences of his early discoveries, first among his patients, then, in society at large. The history of medicine can boast of many physicians who achieved fame by contributing discoveries to the fabric of theoretical science; of others who became known because of their art as clinicians; of still others who organized the policies of public health under which we function today. But few are those, who like Béla Schick, have operated successfully in all three fields of medicine, and who have succeeded in translating their own theoretical scientific studies into clinical skill and social action.

Pasteur, whom Dr. Schick likes to quote, once stated that "To him who devotes his life to science, nothing can give more happiness than making discoveries, but his cup of joy is full only when the results of his studies find practical applications." Mr. Gronowicz's book makes clear that Dr. Schick has been given a full cup of joy, not through some caprice of the gods, but rather as a reward for his long, devoted and good-natured service to medical science and to the welfare of man.

CHAPTER ONE

The First Meeting

A GREY AND MUFFLED FEBRUARY MORNING, 1948. THE STREETS covered with a dirty blanket of snow, churned up by New York's slowly-moving traffic. Not many people about. The "silk-stocking" district. Charming anachronism! But still fashionable to sleep late. Everywhere the wild unpleasant orchestra of shovels on pavement. I shivered from this as much as from the cold, as I lowered my head and scurried on in the direction of the Lexington Avenue subway at 86th Street.

A traffic light stopped me at the corner of Park Avenue. And there I saw it. Half buried in a heap of snow, a scrap of paper smaller than the size of my hand. Curiosity is a habit with me. I stopped and picked it up. "Do not lose this permit —new one costs $1.00," warned the New York State Bureau of Motor Vehicles. Who had lost it? I read the name written in ink. "Dr. Béla Schick, 17 East 84th Street."

I stood musing. Seven years ago I had been preparing a chapter for my book, *Builders of America*, which concerned a Béla Schick. It had led to amusing incidents with librarians, for the women had persisted in calling him Miss Béla Schick, while the male librarians had thought I was hunting up the manufacturer of electric razors. Practically everyone had stumbled over his Hungarian first name which should be pronounced *Bayla*. I had quickly discovered that outside the orbit of physicians and scientists few people knew anything at all of the Dr. Schick I wanted to write about. And yet my Dr. Schick had saved the lives of millions of children throughout the world. His exact observations and remarks concerning the care, feeding and psychology of children had made him one of the world's great pediatricians. No doubt, most educated people have heard of the Schick test for diphtheria, but know nothing of the man who discovered and developed it, while pioneering also in scarlet fever, German measles, serum sickness, allergy, and tuberculosis.

Did this learner's permit belong to the same man? My eyes returned to the yellowish piece of paper in my hand, and I read: "Date of birth: July 16th, 1877; color—white; sex—male; weight—165 lbs.; height—5'6"; color of eyes—brown; color of hair —grey." Yes, that would fit him. But what a prosaic description for a genius.

Without further hesitation, I turned in the direction of Madison Avenue to find the address given on the permit. This scrap of paper had awakened in me a deep desire to meet the scientist whose name should be at the head of the list of pioneers of pediatrics, and who should be as well known to us as Louis Pasteur.

Experimental work on hydrophobia and pasteurization of milk made Pasteur famous. He gave children a better chance to survive. When Béla Schick was only eighteen, Louis Pasteur died. The boy idealized the man. Here was what a great scientist should be.

"It is within the power of civilized man," Louis Pasteur had said, "to cause the infectious diseases to disappear from the earth." Béla Schick was to take this as the motivation of his whole life.

How many random thoughts can pass through the mind in the course of three or four minutes! That was the time I needed to reach the house at 17 East 84th Street. Seeing no doorman, I started to look for the apartment myself. After a few steps to the right I noticed the name on a door, and rang. In spite of the early hour the door was opened immediately. A slender lady of medium height, her hair short and greying, her tailored dress dark. With a smile and without asking any questions, she invited me inside. "Please be seated. The Doctor will be here right away." I stepped inside, fingering my scrap of paper somewhat guiltily. With rapid step she disappeared on the left side of a narrow corridor whose walls were lined with books.

I looked about. On the right was a room that hardly resembled a doctor's office. I stood in the doorway gazing about in astonishment. The room was modern in style; bright warm colors—yellow, red—and scattered over everything a litter of toys, as though some child had been spirited away in the midst of a heavenly game. But these were no ordinary toys. I went in and examined them. On the scales near the bathroom door sat a stuffed panda from Peking. Austrian dolls in bright Tirolese costumes danced on the fluoroscope. On a shelf nearby I found a row of eggs from Yugoslavia, painted with flowers; on a lower shelf china dolls from Germany, snakes and dragons from China, turtles, crocodiles, and the devil knew what kind of African and South American monsters. On the desk, on the chairs, on the window and door frames, everywhere I looked I saw toys, toys from all over the world, and everything I touched sang like an opera singer, squeaked like a mouse, neighed like a horse, or made some startling sound I couldn't describe. The whole menagerie of toys, I was to find out later, had been collected by Béla Schick over a period of a quarter-century.

But curiosity would not let me rest. On the corner of the desk, which was strewn with papers and various little children's knickknacks, stood a high cage completely covered with a cloth painted in Japanese design. Imagining a canary or a parrot inside, I cautiously lifted the cloth—and was startled by a burst of singing from a rainbow-colored bird. I stood entranced before the singing bird, undecided what to do, when I heard a chuckle behind me. I turned to see an elderly, slightly stooped man, gazing at me with twinkling eyes. He was completely happy over my dilemma, and with a quick gesture held out his hand. "A French antique. I got it from Tokyo. Nice, isn't it?"

This was Dr. Béla Schick. I knew it at once from the description. He casually motioned me to a chair, as if it were possible to sit down in any chair without first moving a doll or a music box. As I seated myself the doctor went to the cage, rewound the mechanical bird and replaced the cover. Now it was ready to trap the next inquisitive visitor, I presumed. But my host was chatting easily in his precise English, that had its charming touch of Austrian flavor.

"During World War II, a Viennese friend of mine wandered all the way to Japan. Sadly, he died there. And all that was left of his fortune was this mechanical bird and a fur jacket. These were favorite possessions of his, and before he died he sent them to me. I have received them only just now."

"It is a good time of the year to receive a fur jacket," I said, hoping to prolong the conversation.

The doctor laughed. "It is sad. I don't want to cheat anyone."

"In what way?"

"For me what use is there in a winter jacket? I seldom wear a summer coat, even in the winter, and I never wear a hat."

I had been aware of the liveliness of this man. His gestures and his quick, bright looks all conveyed youthfulness. Yet he was already seventy. Where does he get his secret of youth, I wondered.

My expression was puzzled enough to please him. "It is a matter of habit plus a well-balanced diet," he explained, but with a gesture that made the statement seem a joke. Then he became attentive and serious. "But excuse me, what can I do for you?"

The moment had come. I was embarrassed. After all, it was only a pretense, this carrying a scrap of paper in my hand. I had seen from the beginning that the learner's permit had been issued July 13, 1929. What possible value could it have to him? The paper was already nineteen years old. "Nothing specific," I said, "besides an interesting conversation." And I handed him the permit.

He studied it gravely, then looked up questioningly. I told him where I had found it.

"Shall we say of sentimental value?" he said kindly, and thanked me. Then he added, "As a matter of fact I never had any particular desire to drive. It seems to me that my wife,

Catharine, drives very well. Since I will never do better than she I have left driving alone. But I will keep this card as a souvenir. It will remind me of the fact that I didn't neglect even this endeavor."

"But your license to practice medicine in America, if I am not mistaken, you got without having to pass an examination."

"Yes."

"That was a great acknowledgment," I said trying to keep the conversation going. "Since 1907 only a handful of doctors have received the right to practice without passing the doctors' examination."

He smiled again. "At present I don't practice privately very much. I spend more time working in hospitals."

It was time for me to make a gesture of departure I knew, but I began dramatically, "Before I leave I would very much like to ask you two things . . . ."

"Go ahead, please."

"First, I would like to hear from you, the discoverer, a description of the Schick test, and second, I would like to see the letter in which you were notified of the permission to practice without passing an examination."

I watched the doctor's face closely to see how he would take such a request. There was no sign of disapproval. He evidently thought me sincere. Perhaps he had a liking for medical amateurs.

He was rummaging in a desk drawer. He paused and looked up at me. "This is the shortest description of the test in my words." He waited as I pulled out a pencil and pad. "By the injection of a minute quantity of diphtheria toxin into the skin, it can be determined whether or not an individual is susceptible to diphtheria. No reaction at the place of injection means immunity against the disease. This is called a negative reaction and proves the presence of those substances in the organism which neutralize the diphtheria toxin. In cases where there is a lack of such substances a distinct redness appears at the place where the test was made, and this is called a positive reaction. The latter means susceptibility to diphtheria."

He closed his desk drawer and handed me a letter, which ran as follows:

UNIVERSITY OF THE STATE OF NEW YORK
The State Department of Education
ALBANY

AUGUST S. DOWNING
Assistant Commissioner
and Director of Professional Education

November 26, 1923

Dr. Béla Schick
c/o The Mount Sinai Hospital
5th Ave. & 100th Street
New York City

My dear Dr. Schick:

I have pleasure in advising you that the Board of Regents, at a meeting held November 15, 1923, formally voted to grant you a medical license on approval, because of the eminence and authority which you have attained in your profession.

May I ask you to forward to me at your earliest convenience the original diploma granted you by the University of Graz. In accordance with the statute, this is the document which will be endorsed as a license to practice medicine in this state.

Very sincerely yours,
AUGUST S. DOWNING

As a matter of fact, Dr. Schick was one of the first to receive this honor. Later, similar permission was received by Dr. George Whipple, 1934 Nobel Prize winner for the discovery of the cause of pernicious anemia; Dr. Manfred Sakel, originator of insulin shock for schizophrenia; Dr. Benjamin P. Watson, the director of the Sloane Hospital for Women, Columbia University, known for his achievements in obstetrics and gynecology; and

Dr. Otto Marburg, a famous neurologist who, persecuted by the Austrian Fascists, fled from Vienna in 1938.

This wintry day in the apartment of Dr. Béla Schick was the beginning of a personal acquaintance which soon developed into firm friendship. I got to know his wife, his relatives and friends. I got to know Dr. Schick as a man. In the meantime, by the study of over two thousand books and publications on all the branches of medicine in which he worked, I got to know Dr. Schick as a scientist.

This then is the story of his life and achievements as based on his scientific works, private documents, and long and intimate discussions I have had with him over the past five years.

CHAPTER TWO

The Family Background

JACOB SCHICK WAS A GRAIN MERCHANT OF GRAZ. HE WORKED TOO hard all his life to become caught up in political movements, but he had his ideas on such matters. His thoughts about life were typical of the average man living in the area that had been glued together to form the Austro-Hungarian Empire. An area of 240,000 square miles, it was held into a political unit by the domination of the Hapsburgs, a German-Magyar rule over a mixed group of peoples: Serbs, Slovaks, Croats, Rumanians, Poles, Ukrainians, Slovenes, and Italians.

Men like Jacob Schick, even those who were not so successful in earning a steady income, and who might have experienced some seething discontent against Hapsburg rule, looked across the borders on a German Kaiser and a Russian Czar, and at once felt themselves blessed under the comparatively milder rule of Vienna. And their country, how beautiful it was! What river more lovely than the Danube! What mountains more glorious than the Carpathians! Most of the population lived from the land, felt the wealth of nature in their hearts, and matched the brightness in their dress.

And yet there was no country in Europe, however sheltered, that had not heard the cry of liberty and been stirred. Jacob Schick had a love for France and its art, and for what he imagined was life in Paris. He made a particular point of being called Jacques rather than Jacob. In conversation he supported all social reforms, all efforts of the conquered nations for independence. He gave contributions. He read the progressive press. A vast number of the people around him were doing the same.

The Hapsburgs were not unaware of the dangers in such a situation. The iron rule of Russia and Germany could not be copied in so mixed an empire. They could however adopt the principle of divide and rule: first stir up strife among the Slavs, the Italians, the Hungarians, the Jews, and then ostentatiously interfere in favor of the weak. In this way the Hapsburgs made themselves out to be strong dispensers of justice, while all grudges were deflected from the Vienna court, where a calm and majestic appearance was maintained, festooned by the garish costumes of its dragoons and huszárok.

Jacques was not fooled by claims that the national or even some class conflicts, and the frequent anti-Jewish riots, were spontaneous movements of the people, and he had no need to fear for his own safety. The Slavic and Hungarian peasants liked and admired him. He was generous with his smile and friendly advice; he would pay the highest prices for rye, wheat and oats; he was always good-humored, ready to stop and talk. He made friends wherever he went. Furthermore, his conversation was lively, for he was something of a dreamer, with a Bohemian soul, and was fond of philosophizing.

He was a medium-sized man with broad shoulders, a shapely head, a high forehead above beetling brows and large brown eyes that appeared sad, perhaps because he was only a merchant instead of an artist. His nose was somewhat sharp, refined, and he wore a bristling, drooping mustache. A man of such a nature could never make a fortune. Neither did he starve, and he gave all his children a basic education. His oldest son, Richard, was born in 1876. A year later Béla was born. Then two daughters followed, Frieda in 1888, and Ilona last. All except Béla were born in Graz, at 31 Radetzky Street, where the Schick family lived from 1875 to 1908. Béla was born in Boglar on the shores of Lake Balaton in Hungary, but he very nearly did not live, and that is a story in itself.

Despite his liberal views on politics, Papa Schick was thoroughly conservative in the matter of bringing up children. He believed in strict discipline, and the use of the rod as the surest method. There was no such thing as disobedience in the Schick home; what Jacques wished was law. It never occurred to his children to question or complain. They patterned their behavior after their mother, for not one of them could remember her ever quarreling with their father. Indeed, no man ever made a better choice of a wife. To him she was perfect.

Johanna Pichler—everybody called her Janka, the Slavic equivalent—was young. She was beautiful, with the bright freshness so often found among the local peasant girls, a blonde with large blue eyes, with long eyelashes and delicate brows. Furthermore she dazzled her neighbors with her refined taste in dress, and they considered her without doubt the most attractive woman in Graz. But Jacques was fully aware of it and guarded her jealously. He was proud of her beauty. He liked to show her off. She was rarely permitted to go anywhere without him; social calls, dinners, theaters, picnics, he was always close by. People watched this tall, fair-cheeked, mild-mannered, soft-spoken young woman, and wondered whether she was content with her life. But they could find no undercurrent of sadness. She smiled a lot. She avoided any strong disagreements. She spoke only well of people, and obviously loved her husband deeply. She did not mind his strict treatment of her. He held to outmoded conventions about women and their role in domestic life. It was his way of covering up his jealous nature. But she accepted it as expression of his love.

And so the Schick home was run smoothly and peacefully due to her innate cheerfulness, her psychology in treating her children, and her shining spirit which weathered the occasional periods of financial stress.

When Richard, the first child, was just under one year old, Jacques was perplexed to hear from Janka that she had accepted an invitation to visit Uncle Sigismund of Boglar on the shores of Lake Balaton in Hungary. She knew that he could not leave his business to make such a trip, and he had never permitted his wife to travel alone before. As far as he knew she had never gone against his wishes. She wasn't exactly doing so at this time, but she was putting forward a very good case for going to Boglar alone. His business affairs were going through a trying time. All right, she would be better out of the way. She would be in no danger. She would take little Richard along with her for company. "Besides," she added with an arch expression, "no one will try to flirt with me in my condition."

Jacques looked worried. "But that's just it. There's no knowing when the baby might come. And who will help you then?"

He was not flatly opposing her. She brought out her most powerful argument. "But, Jacques, there is a lot of time still, and when I get there I will be safe—safer with Uncle Sigismund than anyone, for he is a very good doctor."

Her husband admitted that. But there was still the fact of her traveling and living away from him.

But she would be living with her uncle. He would be so pleased to see her and to care for her. And it would be so healthy for her. Janka started to speak of bathing in the lake and of the wealthy, distinguished people from Budapest who come to Boglar every year, but she decided these things were better not stressed.

After lengthy deliberation, Jacques agreed on a compromise, and accompanied her to the town of Barcs, for he had worked that out to be almost the half-way mark between Graz and Boglar. It was the end of April or the beginning of May, 1877, when Jacques waved good-by to his beautiful wife and his baby son Richard, at Barcs.

On July 16, in the house of Uncle Sigismund, a second son was born to the Schicks. The birth was premature, and with complications.

A premature infant, according to a recent statement of the American Academy of Pediatrics, "is one who weighs 2500 grams or less at birth." With his 1500 grams, there was a very slim chance that the Schick baby would live. Doctor Sigismund Telegdy kept it alive. This baby should be called Béla, he decided.

The crisis over, Janka and her baby recovering, Uncle Sigismund came and sat on the bed, looking very serious.

"Janka," he said, "Jacques shall decide the future of your firstborn son."

Of course he would, and she looked up in surprise at her uncle's serious face.

"He can be an engineer," the doctor continued, "a merchant, a farmer or a philosopher—whatever Jacques wants. But, Janka, as for this second son, Béla, you must listen to me. I saved Béla. I say he must be a doctor." After a moment's pause, he added, "Perhaps with my help, a great doctor, one who in his time will save many lives."

CHAPTER THREE

Granduncle and Caesar

DOCTOR TELEGDY WAS A VERY RARE DOCTOR. HE WAS THE ONLY doctor in Boglar, but Boglar did not feel the need of another, for this one was an astonishing machine of energy, all but capable of being in several places at once, while his deep concern for each case won him an ardent devotion from his patients. He seemed to understand all sicknesses. He would deliver at childbirth, cure the aged, even operate, all with the same sure touch, and yet with incredible interest. It was as if he expected each separate problem to lead him straight to some unheard-of medical truth. He was a researcher and a seeker in all fields of medicine. The historian of medicine would have been reminded of Tobias Katz (1652-1729), a mystic and doctor who contributed some interesting observations on infant feeding and child care. Telegdy left no written work, but those who knew him found his diagnoses bold, his methods of treatment heterodox, and, like Tobias Katz's, touched with a mystic sense.

He had torn Béla out of the jaws of death. Now he watched the child grow, never allowing him to escape his influence. This first involuntary vacation of Béla's in Boglar was the beginning of frequent visits to his granduncle Sigismund. At first, Béla came with his mother, but as he grew older he made the journey alone, which suited Jacques a great deal better. The doctor and Béla would spend many hours discussing problems of life, philosophy and particularly medicine. After each such sojourn the boy's parents noticed that he came back in a great state of solemn wisdom. He was becoming more and more determined to follow in his granduncle's footsteps. But he was not sure of his father's feelings on the matter.

Janka was quick to realize that a clash between father and son was inevitable unless Jacques could be persuaded to change his views. Since Uncle Sigismund was only too eager to support Béla as a medical student, Janka tried to appeal to her husband's natural thriftiness. But subtle and expert as were her efforts, they failed. Jacques had his own plans for his two sons. A liberal education they should have, yes, including Gymnasium. Furthermore, they could study dancing and take piano lessons. But first and foremost they must be directed into the grain business. That would give them far more security than any profession. Jacques had plans. He wanted to expand his business —it was possible with two sons to help him. Their future would be made safe then. They would have no worries after he, their father, died.

Jacques informed his wife that he was not opposed to the study of medicine in itself. He knew more about it than she realized. He had wanted to be a doctor himself. He had even been on the eve of studying, before life had changed things for him. He still liked to read books about the history of medicine; the great personalities of the science fascinated him. He could speak of Hippocrates, the father of medicine, with as much delight as a child. He knew that Hippocrates was born in 460 B.C., that he lived to the age of ninety, that he had left a few interesting observations on the feeding of children, that he had recognized many diseases and treated them ably.

As for his contemporaries, Jacques followed their activities very closely, particularly Louis Pasteur and Franz von Soxhlet and their strides forward in the science of feeding children. Dr. von Soxhlet was much talked about at the time in Austria because he introduced maltose in infant feeding, and above all because of his special invention for the sterilization of milk.

Ah yes, Jacques knew all about such things, and it was precisely his knowledge of the medical world that caused him to hesitate when it came to thinking of his son in the profession. Look at the years it would take for Béla to become a doctor, and then the years he would need to build up a well-paying practice. And what proof was there that his son would be successful even then? All Janka's subtle persuasions failed to budge him. Even a letter from Dr. Telegdy had no effect. It was better to play safe and be happy in this world. The grain business would always flourish, for people always have to eat. What simpler and surer enterprise was there than to buy grain in the country, sell it to the city, or grind it in the mill and sell it as flour to the bakeries? Let Béla and Richard work with him in the same business then.

In the evenings he would sit down with his wife and wax eloquent. "I am giving my children a good education. I am even teaching them music. I will have them intelligent. They will be at home in any company. And they will know their trade well, and always live in comfort. With my connections, when they finish their schooling, they will advance to the top of the business." And then with that engaging shift of emphasis that made Janka smile and forget her exasperation, he would say, "Speaking of music, what do you think, Janka? Doesn't Richard play well now? He has talent, he has talent. He should work harder at it."

Jacques made sure that Richard practiced the piano every day. Richard too seemed to grow ambitious, and matters developed to the point that Béla, who liked to play the piano too, hardly ever got the opportunity without the exercise of considerable strategy. He would sneak into the room just before Richard's music lesson began, and spend an hour under the piano waiting for his chance. At the first opportunity, seeing the piano stool free, he would spring into place and bang away at the keys. Even this was not too successful, for Richard would come back. They would fight and scream and cry, and hate each other for hours afterwards.

There was no question of buying a second piano. Janka convinced her husband that something had to be done to divert Béla's attention from music. He loved animals; why not get him a dog? Jacques went out and made a big gesture of it. He returned with a Newfoundland—a big, skinny dog with long, black fur—quite intelligent and very friendly. Béla was delighted. He named the dog Caesar and played with him incessantly. He took Caesar on long excursions, and swam with him in the river Mur.

Richard began to sit up and take notice. In order to play with Caesar once in a while, he had to let Béla play the piano once in a while. A remarkable harmony arose between the brothers. They began studying the piano under the same teacher and learned to play duets together, despite Richard's preference for Wagner and Béla's for Mozart. Béla began to improvise waltzes with Richard, while Caesar lay listening under the piano.

Béla's zeal for composing persisted for a long time. Some of the waltzes he composed later were played by military orchestras of the Austro-Hungarian Empire. He went on to bigger stuff and tackled the writing of opera, but he ended this budding career when he found himself merely rewriting someone else's opera.

One day after a swim in the river, Caesar suddenly fell sick. Béla and Richard carried him up to the house and made a bed for him in the woodshed. According to Béla's diagnosis Caesar had caught a cold. He said nothing to his parents about it, but turning the woodshed into a hospital he set about curing the patient. Caesar got no better. The brothers held a consultation and decided to call in a specialist, the local veterinarian. The man came readily enough, but he failed to help Caesar. When Béla went to the woodshed the next morning he found that his dog was dead.

Béla's curiosity was stronger than his grief. How could he let poor Caesar be buried without knowing what had been the cause of his death? Béla knew that his next move would have to be kept a strict secret, even from his brother. When no one was looking he sneaked into the kitchen and walked out with several table knives of varying sizes. If he was to perform a postmortem examination he would need them sharp. He went in search of the knife and scissors grinder, an itinerant who passed through Graz that day. When everything was ready to his satisfaction, Béla shut himself in the woodshed and prepared to operate, not knowing that the veterinarian had already gone to his parents. But before he could start to work the doctor flung open the woodshed door. Jacques and Janka, behind him, stared in horror at their son. Béla stood guiltily with a knife in his hand.

"Béla," his father began, "Béla . . . ." But something in his son's expression made him hesitate.

"Yes, yes," Béla agreed quickly, "you won't let me do it. Then please, please let me help him." He pointed at the stunned doctor.

"Help him? How help him?" asked his father confused.

"To perform the autopsy."

"Oh no!" There was a look of nausea on Janka's face. "No one has any intention of doing any such thing!"

"The dog died a natural death," his father put in. "Ask the doctor who knows all about animals."

The veterinarian nodded his head. But Béla persisted. Caesar might have died from pneumonia because of his swim in the river.

That same afternoon the veterinarian performed a post-mortem on the dog's corpse. Béla assisted. The official pronouncement read as follows: "Caesar died of natural causes —from old age after bathing in the river."

CHAPTER FOUR

New Theory and Old Practice

"THERE ARE TWO MOST IMPORTANT FACTORS IN THE DEVELOPMENT of children," Dr. Schick told me one day, "environment and education. Children's behavior does not depend on race nor on national origin, as was universally accepted in the European societies between the last two wars, but only on environment. Environment is more consequential than heredity, outside of physical disabilities, which, according to the type of natural infirmity, are decidedly dominating in the mental and physical development of children.

"The first weeks or months at home for the newborn child must be extremely tranquil without noises or constant handling by admiring friends or relatives. Sudden loud voices, quick raising from the bed, interruptions in sleep, or other disturbances of the child's peace categorically influence its delicate nervous system. For example, a sudden fright in infancy may have a far-reaching influence on the emotional life of the child, which later manifests itself in irritability and restlessness or other disorders of the nervous system, often for the entire lifetime.

"Children in their development are reflections of their parents; they are, if you like, mirrors in which one can see the parents. A nervous child usually comes from a home where there is constant tension. A frightened, jumpy child results when there are arguments between the mother and father or between other members of the household. A child absorbs these disturbances in the home with extreme negative results. Often it has an effect on his nervous system for years, and affects his reaction to situations in later life. This is why, ultimately, American psychiatrists have so much to do for grown-up patients who come from broken, disturbed or otherwise unfortunate homes.

"The second important aspect in the child's development, after environment, is education. To simplify matters, let us say geniuses are born, not made, but it still is a fact that suitable good training aids all children, including the prodigies."

Dr. Schick paused for a moment, and I watched a smile play upon his face as he continued.

"We in the United States, I think, especially experiment too much with the educational system. Or, speaking more accurately, there are too many who carry through educational reforms, not knowing whether it will be better for the youngsters or worse, acting on the theory that all reform is improvement.

"Reform is good in everything, provided it is based on past experience; and even then it should be carried out with great care by intelligent people who possess profound knowledge of a child's psyche, and of the cultural, historical, and economic conditions of the society and state. A child has only one education and it shouldn't be trifled with. A good teacher teaches well under any system, but even reform cannot help a bad teacher. There is no substitute for a good one.

"On the way to our goal in life, for every normal person conceives of his life as possessing a goal, we pass three important milestones: education, choice of occupation, and marriage. A bad or inadequate education, an ill-chosen profession, or an unfortunate marriage—any one of these may damage a man or may even completely ruin him. That is why psychiatry is needed for these people. Unfortunately, not all psychiatrists are as capable and conscientious as, for example, my friend, Dr. Alfred Adler. Much of the practice of many psychiatrists is marred by moments of indifference, which may result in further problems in the patient. Too many psychiatrists are incapable, but that 'is another pair of rubbers' as we used to say long ago in Europe."

Taking these remarks of Dr. Béla Schick as a background, I asked him how they fitted in with his own childhood, and he smiled. It was almost as if he were playing a little joke on humanity to have lived so purposefully. Many influences at home had contrived to smooth out difficulties for him as a child. Chiefly? Well, the sense of harmony and contentment which stemmed from the lovely Janka Schick, his mother. Further, he was fortunate enough to have the determined guidance and counsel of that quite unusual man, Uncle Sigismund.

Béla, as a boy, studied for eight years at the Staats Gymnasium in his home town. He was quiet, reserved and studious. When asked many years later if he would write down some interesting experiences of this period, he replied, "Nothing dramatic happened. At home there was peace and quiet, except for small quarrels every now and then with my older brother. And as for school, it was quite routine." He had a great deal of homework. Even his music was neglected far more than he wished. But he was in love. Oh, not with any girl! "The girls didn't fall for me," he later explained, "and I was far too shy to make any friendly gesture toward them." No, his love was for books. He devoured anything his instructors or his mother handed to him. He walked about with a grave expression on his young face, quite locked up within himself. His fellow students for the most part left him alone as a strange boy who had no light conversation and played no games.

His instructors had no complaints. Béla did not neglect his humanitarian studies, his history, literature, Latin, Greek and German, but he had discovered biology and mathematics in books that enraptured him. He searched the Gymnasium library for all the books he could find on these subjects. He began bringing home books on the natural sciences and an occasional history book, and would pore over these long after he had finished his homework. Béla, from the beginning, knew where he was going. That was mainly thanks to Uncle Sigismund.

Looking back on his life in later years, Béla decided that his moments of greatest happiness occurred in his summer vacations at Boglar. The old doctor never failed to invite him. Summer was a more busy time than winter. For here on the shores of Lake

Balaton flocked the fashionable to bathe in the waters and bathe in the sun, and it became a pleasant habit with many of them to become the patients of dear Dr. Telegdy.

Meanwhile Béla was able to breathe the atmosphere of a small-town doctor's home. He assisted Uncle Sigismund as often as he was allowed. At other times he looked on. Each evening after supper the doctor would beckon to Béla, and off they would go for a long walk. The conversation that ensued was completely one-sided, a monologue by the doctor. But young Béla was enthralled. Sigismund would tell stories, mainly about medicine. Béla absorbed them, enlarged his knowledge, and later could himself retell the stories. They generally started with an innocent question, such as: "Who was the first to bring children into the world by the so-called Caesarean section?" And it would turn out that, the day before, this operation had been performed on the wife of a wealthy businessman of Boglar.

The doctor would look quizzically up at the sky, while Béla waited in expectant silence. "Well, it is hard to say, Béla my boy, but over two and a half thousand years ago doctors in India adopted this method. They were very clever, those Indian doctors. Why, do you know they even grafted skin from one part of the human body to another, and did a good job of it too. A huge scar on a man's face? Very well, they would take a section of skin from the man's buttock and graft it on the face. Ah, there was skill and speed in the way they did that, too. There had to be, for they didn't use narcotics to lessen the pain. Oh, they knew of them all right. Narcotics, I mean. But you see the Buddhist teachings wouldn't permit the use of narcotics.

"And I'll tell you more," he went on. "Remember, this was about five hundred B.C. And these doctors in India already had one hundred and fifty surgical instruments. Think of that now. Why, they were able to diagnose almost fifteen hundred different illnesses. For these they had over eight hundred different medicines, which they made mainly from herbs. And as for surgery? Well, they knew how to remove cataracts of the eyes, bladder stones, hernias, tumors."

"What did they study on, Uncle Sigismund? On human corpses?"

"Well, not always. That wasn't easy. For the most part they used dead animals. It took the most courageous doctors—and there were many of them—to get hold of human cadavers for their students to practice on. They did a lot of studying of plant life, too. They learned a lot from that. Water lilies—here they learned about arteries and veins. The gourd—that's the cucumber —helped the study of operations on the stomach. Ah but it's strange, after all that advance in knowledge, the Indian doctors still accepted their 'scientific theory' that the human body is composed of three elements: bile, wind and phlegm. From these three elements, according to their theory, came human blood, bone, flesh, marrow, fat, bile and semen."

Lying in bed that night, Béla would stare up at the ceiling and think over all the things Uncle Sigismund had told him. How difficult it was in ancient India, where medicine was systematically opposed by religion! Look how Buddha himself in his teachings had spoken out against the practice of surgery in the belief that too often it resulted in a kind of murder. Yet despite this, and despite the crushing weight of superstitions and fear among the common people, those doctors who were obstinate enough made incredible gains in the saving of their people from preventable death. Those doctors who were obstinate enough. The words would stick in his head. What was it Uncle Sigismund had said? "In order to arrive at your goal, you must be obstinate. Yes, obstinate, and work very hard."

The grave brown eyes of young Béla stared up at the ceiling and along the walls, as in the half-light of his room he conjured up the visions and hopes of his future life as a doctor. He was happy to think it might be right there in Boglar beside his dear Uncle Sigismund. For was he not seeing how possible it was to be a great doctor in a small town, experimenting unhampered with new and advanced ideas. But, that was it—"you must be obstinate, suffer, search, work . . . work very hard." He would be as obstinate as those doctors of ancient India who worked and worked in spite of Buddha.

CHAPTER FIVE

A Milestone in the Development
of Pediatrics

WHEN BÉLA WAS NOT QUITE EIGHTEEN HE GRADUATED FROM THE
Staats Gymnasium, and in fall of the same year, 1895, he began
the formal study of medicine at Karl Franz University, which
was also in his home town of Graz. Not without struggle did
the boy achieve this aim.

Eight years of study at a Gymnasium in Europe gave the
student a general academic training. He graduated a person
of culture. He knew something about everything, starting with
ancient and classical history; on down through the classic
tongues, Greek and Latin; continuing through modern languages
German and French, and ending with contemporary history,
mathematics, physics and chemistry. He was ready to venture
forth into the world, well equipped to take care of himself,
whether it was to carry on the family business or trade, or to
become an officer of the state.

This was the goal that Jacques had set for his son. With this
he would have been satisfied. But not Béla. Béla wished to go
further. It was vain for his father to argue that more education
was unnecessary, that he did not wish to see his son become
one of the university "drifters," haunted by an aimless urge to

study, shifting from one course to another, unable to find direction, going on for years with no gainful, purposeful employment. Quite obviously Béla was not one of these.

In Béla, his father had to concede, there existed an incredible streak of obstinacy. Nothing, apparently, would swerve the boy from his devotion to medicine. Béla could never be accused of wasting his time at the Gymnasium. What he did not learn at school about medicine he learned from the books he read at home each evening until far into the night. Long before graduating, Béla was sure of which branch of medicine he would concentrate on.

Pediatrics—here was a field full of possibilities, and comparatively new. Why, the first children's hospital ever to be established in the entire world was in 1802 and that was only ninety-three years back. But it was a mere twenty-three years back, in 1872, that the first university courses in pediatrics had been opened. Béla knew how to get his father excited about the subject. It was easy to rattle off information on the history of pediatrics, and he knew his father's fondness for history. Poor Jacques' spluttering protests grew weaker and weaker before the onslaught of delicious facts.

It is incredible how slow we have been, Béla would point out. We have treated our children abominably. We have known things from way back, but we have neglected to expand our knowledge. Only now are we beginning to wake up. Look at this, argued Béla, cornering his astonished father, and he would leap back to the dawn of history. In 1555 B.C., or about that time, the Ebers Papyrus spoke of healing eye sickness in children, of how to strengthen the flow of milk in a nursing mother, and of how to kill worms in a child's abdomen.

And look at the Talmud, Béla would continue, as if he were waving the pages before his father's eyes. The Talmud has many things to say about the care of children, and how to feed them. Why, the Talmud says—and how beautifully, too—"The world is kept alive by the breath of children."

Béla would pour into his father's ear the names of the "obstinate" men, who sowed the seeds of modern pediatric knowledge—Hippocrates, Soranus of Ephesus, Aetius, Paulus of

Aegina, Rhazes, Oribasius, Avicenna. He spoke of the *Syriac Book of Medicine*, and of the books of the Hindus. He quoted the observations on children of that Roman scholar and philosopher, Celsus, who lived during the reign of Augustus Caesar, and he provided his father with his own translation:

There are certain disorders that show themselves at various stages in life. Many children may be bothered with inflammations in the area around the navel, vomitings, waking at night, discharges in the ears or spreading sores of the mouth, which the Greeks call aphthae. Some of the more common complaints during the cutting of the canine teeth are: slight fevers, convulsions, diarrhea, teething, and abcesses of the gums. Children who suffer these discomforts are those who are very much bound about the stomachs and have the best habits. As they grow older, the youngsters are harassed by disturbances of the glands, various curvatures of the spine, swellings of the lymphatic glands, uncomfortable warts, which the Greeks knew as acrochordones, and other types of nodules and growths. The above-mentioned disorders and others, including prolonged fevers and bleeding from the nose, manifest themselves at the onset of puberty.

It may be stated that the most perilous periods for youngsters in general are those that occur around the fortieth day of their life, the seventh month, the seventh year, and finally the period which coincides with their individual time of puberty. Any disorder or derangement of faculties or functions may continue for a long or extended time if they have begun during infancy and have not been ended with puberty, or by a man's first relations with a woman, or with the first advent of the menses in females. These disorders are usually terminated by the means mentioned above.

Béla would then speak of Aretaeus of Cappadocia, the Greek scholar, writer and philosopher living in the second century A.D., one of the greatest diagnosticians known to ancient history. Detailed accounts and records were left by Aretaeus on tetanus, pneumonia, empyema, abscess of the tonsils, diphtheria and angina. His short and straightforward sentences brought clear light to such complex disorders as insanity, apoplexy, cerebral paralysis and hysteria. Now here was one of the "obstinate" men. Like Hippocrates. They fought against prejudices and open opposition. They had no tradition to back them up. What they said and what they wrote down was true to them because of their own conviction, and this conviction came from their own observations and conclusions.

The brave and obstinate men who followed them added bit by bit to this background of knowledge, and out of it the study of pediatrics developed as a special field. It is reported that Galen, for instance, from his studies in the last half of the second century A.D., was able to give a detailed report on rickets and on the treatment of children with various cases of worms. And there was the Arabian physician, Rhazes, who published a treatise on smallpox and measles; he also made interesting comments on protecting the eyes of the newborn and on diarrhea in infants. Then at last in Italy in the year 1472 the first book ever published on pediatrics appeared under the title *Libellus de Egritudinibus Infantium*: A Small Book on Infants' Diseases.

The author of this monumental work was born in the city of Padua. His name was Paulus Bagellardus. He studied philosophy and medicine at the university of his own city, then taught medicine there for thirty years before he moved to Venice. The fame of Bagellardus as a healer spread all over Europe. But Béla could tell his father little of the man's personal life, for very little is known, except that he pursued the study of architecture as a hobby and had a mania for restoring porticoes on the mausoleums of wealthy and revered Italians.

Béla, in his campaign to convert his father, began leaving books around in the hope that they would be read, particularly *The Children's Book*. This was a work on pediatrics written by a surgeon of Basel, Felix Würtz (1518-1576). It became enormously popular, a sort of encyclopedia for mothers. It had to be printed again and again to keep up with the demand, and was translated into both English and French. Béla found it fascinating reading, and he knew his father would too if it once caught his attention. He would leave the book open at such places as the following, here given in its old English translation by Abraham Lenertzon Fox:

> For a warning I will give a hint of the faults committed by Nurses, in their rude manner of washing Children's mouthes, whereby they do and have caused this great mischief unto Children.
>
> Some indiscreet people take wool or rough linen or the bath cloth out of the bath, feel with it to the throat, and wash it saying, how furr'd is Child in the throat, I must wash off that white stuff and rub it so hard that they pull off their subtile skin, even as a soft rind is peeled off the tree, which if once done, then the next day his mouth groweth more white, which if they see it, then they feel further into the mouth, and fall on washing of his mouth, saying, this Childs tongue looks white, I must scrape his tongue, and scrape and wash away the tender skin of his tongue, and make it bleed, which surely causeth the trush in the mouth, and the more they go on in their washing, the worse they make it.
>
> This great fault about the mouth washing, hath moved me to write this Treatise, and I intreat all good people not to make use of such washing, and to warn others from it also: for the tongue doth cleanse itself, being a member which is still in motion, and groweth not weary.

Or perhaps a section like this, entitled "Of Crooked and Lame Children, Coming Thus into the World," which concluded with this bit of poetic whimsy:

> Have a care you bind the Joint not too hard,
> then surely is done neither hurt nor smart.
> Do not begrudge your time at all,
> a timely cure on the party will fall.
> Be exact with your tying and setting,
> then the crooked Joint will right come in.
> Give not over, be willing, not timorous,
> The Joint grow'th right as a wick most curious.

Béla could speak most eloquently to his father on that great contemporary of John Milton, Thomas Sydenham, who wrote in his first book: *Methods of Treating Fevers, Based on His Own Observation* that "The physician should be devoted above all things to the welfare of the human race . . . . The physician should bear to the same laws of mortality and disease as others; and he will care for the sick with more diligence and tenderness if he remembers that he himself is their fellow-sufferer."

Sydenham was born in 1624 in Dorsetshire, England, in the tiny village of Wynford Eagle. But at the age of eighteen he had already matriculated as a Fellow Commoner in Magdalen Hall, Oxford. It was a time of terrible unrest throughout the country. Open strife broke out through the land between supporters of the king and those who would limit his powers. No university was unafflicted by the bitter hatreds, and many times young Thomas found his studies broken into and himself involved in the campus battles between the Royalists and the adherents of Parliament. In one of these frays he was wounded, while open warfare throughout the country struck down his mother and his two brothers.

Thomas finally received his Bachelor of Medicine degree from Wadham College in April, 1648, and settled down to practice as a physician in the Westminster quarter of London, not far from John Milton, whose poetry he glorified. But he was a man of strong opinions, and envied for his great learning. He began to be called "the English Hippocrates." His outspokenness and his unorthodoxy whenever he felt the need for new thought created many enemies. Béla exulted in this side of Thomas' life. Here was one of the "obstinate" men. Look what Dr. Andrew Brown, who worked closely with Thomas Sydenham, said of his friend's difficulties at the College of Physicians:

> He had only gained the sad and unjust recompense of calumny and ignominy, and that from the emulation of some of his Collegiate brethren, and others, whose indignation at length did culminate to that height, that they endeavored to banish him, as guilty of medical heresies out of that illustrious Society.

But the opposition of dull-witted, hard-headed influential doctors had no effect on Thomas, whose studies of measles, scarlet fever, epilepsy in children, smallpox, rickets, convulsive coughs, and scurvy advanced medical knowledge in these fields enormously. In the treatment of smallpox he introduced the so-called "cooling method" and in the treatment of malaria he was one of the first to use medicinal barks.

Sydenham gained a reputation for his engaging remarks. The best book to begin medical studies with is *Don Quixote*, he said, and at another time: "The arrival of a good clown exercises a more beneficial influence upon the health of a town than that of twenty asses laden with drugs."

His observations on chorea were so profound and so accurate that to this day it is called Sydenham's Chorea to distinguish it from the generally styled chorea major, or St. Vitus' Dance. Béla could quote Thomas Sydenham at length on this subject: "This is the kind of convulsion, which attacks boys and girls from the tenth year to the time of puberty. It first shows itself by limping or unsteadiness in one of the legs, which the patient drags. The hand cannot be steady for a moment. It passes from one position to another by a convulsive movement, however much the patient may strive to the contrary. Before he can raise a cup to his lips, he makes as many gesticulations as a mountebank; since he does not move it in a straight line, but has his hand drawn aside by spasms, until by some good fortune he brings it at last to his mouth. He then gulps it off at once, so suddenly and so greedily as to look as if he were trying to amuse the lookers-on."

Béla would seek to make his father laugh by the story of Sir Hans Sloane, later the founder of the British Museum, who as a young man was sent to Sydenham with a letter of recommendation discribing him as an unusually intelligent and talented student, especially versed in anatomy, botany, and other allied subjects, who now wanted to study medicine. The noted doctor read through the letter in silence, then turned to Hans. "This is all very fine," he said, "but it won't do. Anatomy! Botany! Nonsense! Sir, I know an old woman in Covent Garden who understands botany better; and as for anatomy, my butcher can dissect a joint just as well. No, young man, all this is stuff. You must go to the bedside. It is there alone you can learn disease."

It was a good argument for Béla, too, for he had his Uncle Sigismund who let him work at "the bedside" with him in his practice at Boglar. No—he, Béla, would not be content with a bundle of theories. He would be out practicing, experimenting. It was the "obstinate" men who succeeded. Look at the story of Edward Jenner (1749-1823). He discovered smallpox vaccination, but not easily. "They who are not in the habit of conducting experiments," he wrote, "may not be aware of the coincidence of circumstances necessary for their being managed so as to prove perfectly decisive; nor how often men engaged in professional pursuits are liable to interruptions which disappoint them almost at the instant of their being accomplished." And he continued, "The spring of the year 1797, which I intended particularly to have devoted to the completion of my investigation, proved, from its dryness, remarkably adverse to my wishes; for it frequently happens, while the farmers' horses are exposed to the cold rains which fall at that season that their heels become diseased, and no Cow-pox then appeared in the neighborhood."

Dr. Jenner transferred cowpox matter from the arm of a woman who had been infected, and injected it into the arm of an eight-year-old boy. Six weeks later, Dr. Jenner injected smallpox matter into the arm of the boy, and the youngster did not develop the disease. He had become immune.

But perhaps Béla's favorite subject at that time was the work that had been done on another of the most dreaded of child diseases. Given the name "diphtheria" by Pierre F. Bretonneau in the first part of the nineteenth century, the disease had been known as long ago as the sixth century, as the writings of Aetius show.

Aetius (502-575 A.D.) came from the town of Amida in Mesopotamia. Doctor and officer of the guard at the Byzantine court, he left many written dissertations in the sphere of ophthalmology, gynecology, obstetrics, surgery, and pediatrics. And he wrote of diphtheria:

The disease in youngsters is invariably a consequence of pre-existing aphthae. The open sores change color and are at times white and patchy, while at other times they appear to be grey, or they seem to be similar to the scabs brought about by the use of the cautery. The afflicted person complains of a dryness in the throat and labored breathing, which is especially pronounced when there is a redness under the chin. After the intense period is over, noma and gangrene ensue. In countless occurrences the uvula is dissipated and, if the ulceration ceases and cicatrization ensues, the afflicted youngsters speak with confusion, and when they attempt to swallow, liquid comes back out through the nasal passages. In the majority of cases, the dangerous period lasts until the seventh day.

A detailed account of the disease in children was given by the great eighteenth century pediatrician, Nils Rosén von Rosenstein, professor at the University of Upsala and later at Stockholm University. Andrew Sparrman translated his book into English, and it was published in London in 1776. Von Rosenstein said of diphtheria:

When children are affected with this disease they lose their usual cheerfulness, are something hot, and some of them cough; they complain of a slight obtuse pain in the windpipe somewhat below its orifice; and opposite the same place, on the outside of the throat, there is a little swelling to be observed in some patients, which aches a little on pressing it with the finger; the face begins to look red, and is puffed up; nothing extraordinary is to be seen on inspecting the fauces, and there is seldom any difficulty of swallowing, but the breath is laborious; a fever comes on, with a hard and very quick pulse; the thirst becomes pressing; the patient coughs sometimes. All this increases hostility, and on a sudden the pulse lowers, and grows very rapid, but weak; the breathing becomes more difficult, frequent and shorter; the pain disappears, the coughing ceases, and death comes on unexpectedly.

Béla knew the full history of experiments with this disease. He would speak of bacteriologist Edwin Klebs, his discovery of the bacillus of diphtheria under a miscroscope; of bacteriologist F. A. J. Löffler who managed to isolate the bacillus and demonstrated its growth in animals. These men were still living. The work was still going on. It was only six years ago, Béla pointed out, that Émile Roux and Alexander Yersin, working in Pasteur's laboratory, had discovered a toxin produced by the diphtheria bacillus. And now an antitoxin had been discovered by Emil von Behring and S. Kitasato but only five years ago. The disease would soon be conquered because of men like that, and Béla explained to his father he would like to be one of these men. Why not?

Jacques was dumbfounded by his son's erudition and his zeal. He glanced at his wife who had averted her eyes, and he threw up his hands. Béla went to the university.

CHAPTER SIX

Professor Kraus

AT THE KARL FRANZ UNIVERSITY IN GRAZ THE EIGHTEEN-YEAR-OLD Béla Schick began his study of medicine in earnest. He fell at once under the spell of a very unusual professor. This was Friedrich Kraus, head of the Clinic for Internal Medicine. Dr. Kraus was not only a noted clinician, but a teacher of rare qualities. He seemed to take a personal interest in every one of his students. He did not seek to dominate or coerce them. He took them into his confidence, treating them almost as if they were his equals. If he raised his voice it was rarely in anger, for his patience seemed never to wear out. It would be for dramatic purposes, to illustrate the importance of a point.

Dr. Kraus was only thirty-seven at the time. He had come from Vienna to accept the position in Graz only a year before and he had immediately made an impression by a lecture entitled "Hippocratismus," which was based on the Hippocratic theory that normally an illness is not confined to certain organs of the human body, but rather affects the entire human system. The basic function of the doctor, he emphasized, is to be a healer. He must love the role of healer. He must, if necessary, utilize various therapeutic mediums, in order to treat the patient both physically and psychologically. But, he went on, the true clinician must apportion his time into three fundamental divisions: research, healing, teaching. And in each of these three he must be the master. The good clinician, he reiterated, cannot divide the body into sections, just because of the special mechanical devices existing to treat certain sections of the body. The clinician must work with the minimum number of methods. He should use mechanical means of healing only when absolutely necessary.

Young as he was, Friedrich Kraus had a great deal of experience, both in study and teaching, in chemistry, physiology and biology. He was a pupil of Professor Kahler of the University of Prague and Vienna, who treated young Friedrich as though he were his own son and impressed upon him all his knowledge, experience and love of mankind.

Friedrich's success at Karl Franz University was therefore assured. He taught his young students proper methods of working in the laboratory and clinic. He inspired them to reason for themselves and freely passed out his own theories and observations for them to investigate. His clinic at the university soon became known all over Europe and under his guidance emerged such great physicians as Hans Eppinger, Scholz and Pfeifer.

Each Monday and Wednesday morning from 8:15 to 9:15 Professor Kraus would carry on a clinical demonstration, and for the hour that followed a polyclinic to which his assistant would bring cases for diagnosis by the students. Tuesdays, Thursdays and Fridays, from 8:15 to 10:00 A.M., he devoted his energy and time to working in the clinic with his assistants and his students. And all the students looked forward to Saturdays when their professor spent an hour and a half presenting the results of experiments on animals, and discussing the clinical work done during the week. He was a gifted speaker, a rare accomplishment in learned scholars. He know how to excite and inspire his audience.

His lectures on themes such as the circulatory apparatus, tuberculosis, and diseases of the thyroid gland were coupled with demonstrations, and many times he would seem to be digressing from his theme, scattering brilliant observations and remarks which kept his eager listeners on the edges of their seats. These sidelights, apparently thrown out with such ease, would form the foundation for advanced work by his assistants and students.

Though Professor Kraus was truly amiable and benevolent, he purposely cultivated the reputation of being stern and severe and demanding. He was never known to flatter his students, even the most capable and talented among them. During an examination when a faltering student started out with "I believe . . ." Professor Kraus exploded. "Believe! You don't know? To believe is to doubt. One must know at least fifty per cent of the facts, even to guess correctly."

But when he saw symptoms of original thought in the classroom or in the laboratory he would be overcome with a burst of happiness, seize the student responsible and embrace him heartily. Then he would repeat his favorite maxim: "Think and act quickly! Think quickly and accurately and act quickly. Then you will become good physicians."

When a quiet and thoughtful youth named Béla Schick came to his classes, Professor Kraus became at once aware of the immense concentration of the boy and of his tireless study. He began to count on Béla to assist him in experiments, and serve as an example for other students. He treated Béla as an equal, and talked him into more precise and exacting work in the laboratory. Béla became completely immersed. Nothing else in life seemed to interest him. Even the thought of Boglar seemed to have faded.

In the meantime Janka was getting letters from Boglar regularly. In each letter Uncle Sigismund talked of his plans as soon as Béla had finished his study at the university. Béla would come to Boglar, and bit by bit Uncle Sigismund would let Béla take over the practice. The wealthy visitors to Boglar would be much attracted to Béla. Béla would be rich, with a fine practice. And he, Dr. Sigismund Telegdy, would sit back and be happy.

Janka felt obliged to talk to Béla about it. After all, it was only reasonable. Béla would have to find some way of living after he left the university. But Béla shrugged it off. This was no time, he said, for him to be thinking of what he would do so far ahead. Janka insisted. One had to look ahead. Some day Béla would get married to some nice girl and would want to have a family. How was he going to do that if he had no practice after leaving the university? Studying was all very well, but some practical measures must be taken.

But Janka had to give up. She could get nothing out of her son but "wait and see." She sighed resignedly, for she could see no way of penetrating that deep mood of preoccupation into which Béla had got himself ever since he came under the influence of that young professor Friedrich Kraus. Then a sudden smile played on Béla's full lips. "Uncle Sigismund wants me enough," he said. "He'll be willing to wait. The girls don't want me at all, so there's no point of thinking in terms of a family of my own. And for all I know," he went on quickly, "the medical profession may not want me, deciding that I cannot accomplish anything interesting enough for them."

"Well, evidently Professor Kraus thinks differently," his mother cut in.

"The Professor can think what he wants to," Béla replied stolidly. "Look how many professors up to now have made mistakes, and in more significant matters than the career of a *voluntarius*, helping out in the labs."

Janka had no alternative but write still another letter to Uncle Sigismund pacifying him with noncommittal words.

CHAPTER SEVEN

"... Pediatrics Is My Life."

THAT WARM JULY EVENING AT THE HOME OF THE SCHICKS AT 31 Radetzky Street was unusually noisy and merry.

From the dining room came the high voice of eleven-year-old Frieda. Helping the servant set the table, she felt it necessary to sing out at the top of her lungs some melody she had heard while playing in the streets. In the drawing room Richard was doing his best to drown her out by switching climactically from Mozart to Wagner on the piano.

Janka, in the kitchen, supervised the steaming pots and the oven where a stuffed goose was roasting. At the threshold of the spacious kitchen stood Jacques, his voice loud above the din. Standing with him listening to his analysis of the vast difference between his two sons, Richard and Béla, was Uncle Sigismund. The old doctor was in a very amiable mood, leaning against the wall, letting his eyes wander about, sometimes watching the efficient Janka and sniffing the glorious aroma of warm cakes and roasting goose, and sometimes watching the antics of little Ilona, circulating without apparent purpose as she shrieked in various voices, now imitating her sister, now playing some monstrous steam train. It pleased him to see the immaculate quality of everything about the house. Janka sensed his approving eye, and felt happy. For no one knew better than she what this meant, the arrival of Uncle Sigismund, who so rarely traveled, on the eve of Béla's birthday.

The only one needed to complete the family picture was Béla himself. Béla was late, but then that was not unusual these days. There were so many different places he might have gone to—the hospital, the library. There was even a chance that he had gone for a stroll with someone, with some young lady. Oh, that was possible *now!* Béla was twenty-two, as studious as ever, but certain changes had come over him. His mother had guessed the thing from the moment it started, but it took Richard to bring the subject out into the open. For Richard had come upon Béla one day on the outskirts of the city, astonished to find his brother out strolling with a girl. The two were talking quite animatedly, but Béla when quizzed by his brother as soon as he got home denied flatly that there was anything more significant than an intellectual bond. So Béla rather stiffly explained, and held to his ground.

But there was a plot afoot. It was not natural, his mother reasoned, for a boy—no, a man—of his age not to be interested in the opposite sex, and not to think of a family and home of his own. She listened anxiously as Richard began to tease his brother by asking when he was going to get married. Even their father began to make heavy jests. Janka wondered whether all this would help Béla.

Béla's reaction had been a silent indifference at first, almost a sullen refusal to communicate. Then at last Janka detected what she was so anxiously waiting for. Béla suddenly began to pay more attention to his clothes. They had to be neatly pressed. His shoes had to be polished to a fine lustre. His collar had to be changed every day. He grew a small mustache which he tended each morning. Richard grew tired of trying to get a rise out of his brother, and Jacques had given up the struggle. But Janka saw, and she was pleased. Béla was attempting to make himself agreeable to some certain person.

Each morning, Janka surveyed the appearance of her studious son as he left for the university. He was not a tall man, but he was well built and had an intelligent-looking face with a pleasant smile. Above all he had wonderful eyes. Wonderful, Janka thought, because they seemed so sincere. And Béla was sincere, sincere in whatever he did—his studies, his career, even this new-found interest, this girl he was trying to impress. She knew that for certain. And any explanation that Béla might give, such as the one he gave to his brother on the first questioning—that it was "only a matter concerning the Clinic for Internal Medicine"—such an explanation, she knew, was just Béla's natural desire to keep himself unexposed, a sort of preserving of his sincerity.

This very evening then, July 15, when Béla was late Janka could still tell herself that if Béla was late it was for some good reason; perhaps this girl, she hoped. But Béla was unusually late. Little Ilona had finished her imaginary train-ride hours ago and had gone to bed immediately after her supper. Frieda was also in her room. Finally, Richard, his father and mother and Uncle Sigismund arranged themselves around the table to enjoy a delayed supper.

"Just a few minutes more, only a minute or two . . . and Béla will come," Janka was saying, as she nervously straightened the flower-embroidered collar on her black dress. And as if in answer to her plea, the door was heard to slam and in rushed Béla with flowers in his hands. He seemed to be moved by an inner excitement; greeted his family with a brief flourish and seemed confused before his beloved Uncle Sigismund.

Supper began in silence. The others were waiting for an explanation. Béla was eating fast. He appeared to be in deep thought. He made no attempt to speak until he had finished his soup. Then he straightened, and looked across at his mother. He smiled and began his story.

He had gone to the home of Professor Escherich. Of course everyone knew who Professor Theodor Escherich was! The professor had greatly interested himself in Béla. He was frank to say that he envisioned a great future in medicine for the young student. When Béla had gotten into the Neurological and Psychiatric Department, too fascinated in all branches of the subject to realize that he was moving away from his original intention, it was Professor Escherich who had brought him back to the right direction. Béla must study under him, in the Pediatric

Department. The field needed the type of student Béla was. Béla never ceased being grateful to him for his understanding and his encouragement.

This night the professor had invited him to his own home to meet Dr. Meinhard von Pfaundler, who had a considerable reputation as a scholar and lecturer, and who was to deliver lectures at Karl Franz the following year. Béla was astonished to find von Pfaundler a very young man, only five years older than himself in fact. He seemed to have all the gifts. Youth, presence, originality of thought. Béla was awed. Could he ever be like that? Before he had reached the age of twenty-one von Pfaundler had investigated the anatomy of the suprarenal glands, and at twenty-eight he made a special study of the gastric capacity of infancy and childhood. Here was a man who was traveling swiftly along the road that Béla wanted to take. Béla eagerly plied him with questions. When von Pfaundler left the Escherich home he invited Béla to walk along with him and talk further some more. Béla lost all track of time. His new-found friend was a genius at making his own work exciting. He talked as confidently as though he held the future in his hands. As though he already foresaw a brilliant and constructive career.

To digress a moment and look into the destiny of this new young friend of Béla's, let it be said that in 1902 he became Extraordinary Professor of Pediatrics at the Karl Franz University of Graz, and four years later a professor at the University of Munich. His pediatric clinic in that city was one of the best in the world, and his private library was to grow to be one of the largest in Europe. His writings were of high significance to the medical world. In 1916 he completed a book entitled *Studies of Body Measurement in Children,* and eight years later *Physiology, Nutrition and Care of the Newborn.* He was the co-editor with Dr. Schlossman of the ten-volume *Handbuch der Kinderheilkunde.* He ended his astonishingly brilliant career in 1947 at seventy-five.

But back in 1899, walking with Béla from Professor Escherich's home, his great enthusiasm lay in his investigation of spinal puncture in children. He had just completed his papers on the subject and had shown them to Professor Escherich. His enthusiasm was quite infectious, and Béla's ambitions rose every minute. There was so much to be done, thought Béla, so much before him, so little time to do it all. He must study harder. Nothing must be allowed to get in his way.

This was how he was speaking at the table before his family and the gravely silent Dr. Telegdy. He was to complete his studies at Karl Franz University in May of the following year, yet now he was talking about the necessity of spending a few more semesters attending the lectures of von Pfaundler, perhaps working closely with him in the laboratory.

Béla was so taken up with his own enthusiasm that he was obviously unaware of the reaction of his listeners. Their profound silence had no special meaning to him, although he felt pleased that they did not interrupt him. But Janka's heart sank. What had become of all those fond hopes for her son? Had she been completely deluded when she watched the changes in Béla? Was there after all no pretty young girl waiting to marry him? How many more years was Béla to immerse himself in cold studies? Her plans for him were falling apart, all so suddenly.

As for Jacques, he felt a sullen frustration. What was happening, what he had allowed to happen, was what he had wanted the most not to happen. A son of his drifting, a scholar poking among dusty books, penniless, futureless. Yet somehow he had lost control of this son of his. There was no influence he could assert. Outside of disowning him, refusing him all financial assistance—and this Janka would never countenance, even if it could be proved to be for his own good—there was nothing to do but bow to Béla's wishes.

But when Janka and Jacques turned to Uncle Sigismund, they could not divine his thoughts. Surely he had most to lose. He was no longer a man of super-abundant energy. His life would not go on for much longer. He had put so much trust in the thought of Béla coming to Boglar, taking over his practice, becoming a successful active general practitioner among the wealthy, free from financial worries, free to experiment as he wished. He had expected great enthusiasm from Béla for what he wanted to present him. But now it seemed Béla was lost to him. Perhaps someone else would have to take his place on the picturesque shores of Lake Balaton.

Richard, after finishing supper, rose from the table without a word and went to the living room to the piano. In a moment the sounds of Chopin's Funeral March were heard. Janka was appalled. She went quickly to the door and hushed him up. Coffee was served by the maid. At last Béla was beginning to grasp that all was not well with his family. He dropped into sudden and awkward silence and looked at his mother. Janka avoided his eyes and looked at Uncle Sigismund.

After a moment's pause, Dr. Telegdy pushed his chair back and stood up. "On the occasion of your birthday, Béla, my boy," he began, "and on the occasion of your decision not to become an ordinary country doctor, but a scholar, I extend to you my heartiest felicitations." He walked round the table. Béla got up, confused. Uncle Sigismund wrapped both his arms about Béla, as he continued, "In case you ever need help, Béla, always know you can count on me." He drew out of his pocket a large gold watch on a heavy gold chain and handed it to Béla. "Best wishes on that hard road."

Béla found tears in his eyes. It had changed the mood of the room. Opposition to his plans had magically vanished. Adjourning to the living room, Béla could talk freely about his work at the university, and he found Uncle Sigismund a most sympathetic listener. The pale fears of Janka had melted away. Richard said solemnly, "Well, I think I shall have to capitulate. I must admit that my brother is smarter than I am. Some day I shall be proud that I have the same name."

"I don't know what will happen to that pride," Béla smiled quietly, "but there is one thing I am certain of—pediatrics is my life."

CHAPTER EIGHT

In the Army

WITH THE TURN OF THE CENTURY BÉLA COMPLETED HIS STUDIES
at Karl Franz University. It was springtime. His future lay before him, resting mainly on high hopes. In those days it was
said of one completing his studies at a school of higher education—"He is already smart and free." But what was freedom if
he had no money, and for him to have money meant a good
profitable medical practice. There were many of his fellow students who would have been satisfied with just that for the rest
of their lives. And here again it was being offered to Béla without any effort on his part, for Uncle Sigismund never lost hope
that Béla would turn to Boglar.

Yet after all was done it remained Béla's decision. And secretly Uncle Sigismund knew how hard a decision it was. It was
a kind of selfishness for him to want Béla in Boglar. The other
path was to possible fame and eminence as a great doctor, and
it was the path he himself might have taken, and secretly
wished he had. But he knew and Béla knew what it entailed,
how much it would cost. Those who dedicate their lives to
teaching and study rarely, if ever, attain wealth. Often it means
the sacrifice of their own private lives to study. It can be a
lonely and hard road, and at the end it can mean failure.

The summer passed for Béla in uncertainty. By October he

was in the army. The decision could be postponed for six months more.

For those six months he had to serve in the Medical Division of the Austro-Hungarian Army stationed at the fortress at the mouth of the river Waag which flowed into the Danube. The name of the fortress suffered much from the various tongues pronouncing it. If some document had to be filed by an Austrian or German, the name would be written Komarn. If a Hungarian wrote it, it became Komárom, while the Slovak in his own manner wrote Komarno. Originally it was a Slovak town founded during the Roman Empire, and to this day is still surrounded by forests, by crumbling castles, remnants of defensive walls and other relics of the Middle Ages.

In those early days Komarno was an important port. It trafficked in hides and skins, timber, silk, cereals, spices and wine. The southern Slavs would trade here with their northern and eastern cousins, German and French travelers would stop over on their journeys to the Near East, as did the Turks and Tartars going the other way. But the small glory of Komarno did not last for long after the sixteenth century. During the years 1543-1663 the fortress was besieged four times by the Turkish Army. Devastating earthquakes attacked the town in 1735 and 1738, and in the following century the revolution of '48, the cry of European peoples for bread and for freedom, caught up the Slovaks of Komarno. As usual the reply of the ruling despots was to supply the people with lead from their arsenals. Komarno Fortress was no exception.

Once the townsmen were suppressed they stayed suppressed, and the fortress remained strong. The drafted soldiers under the leadership of professional officers saw to it that the minds and souls of the hard-working people religiously and correctly thought and felt for the "noble and benevolent Emperor" Franz Josef.

Compulsory service brought Béla Schick into this machinery of control, but traditional army customs worked to his advantage. Persons of higher education who practiced their professions in the service, such as doctors, engineers, chaplains, were given the rank of officer. The rank of officer, like an aristocratic title, awakens awe in oppressed peoples, it was reasoned. Further, it helps build up a caste system within the army. Out of such comes obedient and blind discipline—the basic cement with which the Austro-Hungarian nations were held together. And so Béla was made a captain of the Medical Division, caring for the health of the officers and men at Komarno Fortress.

Conditions for experimental medical work at the fortress were nonexistent. There was little for Béla to treat beyond the average ailments in the life of a soldier. His cases were venereal diseases, stomach disorders, headaches. Occasionally he had to make a suture of a soldier's broken head, or give an injection. But there was definitely not enough to keep Béla from growing restless. He tried to fill the gap by perusing medical books and periodicals he had subscribed to from Vienna and Berlin, and he dreamed continually of the work he would do at the university in Vienna or even in Graz.

During leisure hours, Béla refused to join his fellow officers in drinking and card-playing. He attached himself to the Military Band. On the piano he would compose new waltzes and marches for the band to play. These were received with acclaim; many of his compositions were picked up outside the fortress and soon became part of the repertoire of Austro-Hungarian Army bands.

Music was good for his own soul. It released his creative energies which could so easily have remained stultified for those six months. This much was plain to Béla, and he realized also that others needed some release of this kind. So often it was the lack of it that drove a soldier to drinking too heavily, or resulted in nervous disorders. He began experimenting with the idea of music as therapy, prescribing, in place of alcohol, musical sessions with the military orchestra.

The success of these experiments made a profound impression on Béla. From that time on he tried always to have a piano in his consulting room, not only so that he could play during leisure moments, but particularly for the benefit of his youthful patients. One of the first questions he would ask a five- or six- or seven-year-old visitor was whether he or she knew how to play the piano. If the answer was in the affirmative, Béla would sit at the piano beside the youngster and proceed to play a duet. Every melody, even those heard but once, he was able to play from memory, and thus built up amazement and enthusiasm in the child. By winning his young patients' confidence and putting them at ease he was better able to begin his diagnosis.

But back at Komarno Fortress thanks to music the half year passed by swiftly enough, and Béla, curling up his dark, short mustache, soon packed his bags for the return trip to Graz, his head crammed with dreams of studies and plans for the future. Nothing now, he felt, could change his stubbornness, his sober realism. Let him be called one of the "obstinate" men. Let Uncle Sigismund who first used the phrase understand it in him. He knew what he wanted of life. The consequences might be tragic. Nevertheless, he must go on.

CHAPTER NINE

A Surprise for Béla

RELEASED FROM SERVICE, RETURNING TO GRAZ AND HIS FAMILY, Béla began to feel the inevitable touch of depression. Eager and ready for great work, vast achievements, yet he was faced with the reality of having nothing immediate to do, no tangible prospects. His family rejoiced to see him. They asked no pointed questions, but he felt their watching. The great decision loomed before him once again. There was always Uncle Sigismund. He owed a great deal to Uncle Sigismund. Uncle Sigismund was wise and experienced and successful. It was not easy to ignore the call from Boglar. Ignore it for what? There were no tangible prospects.

The restlessness and indecision that gnawed at him were the force compelling his steps on that particular day to the Clinic for Internal Medicine. He would get the advice of his former professor, the brilliant, efficient, Dr. Friedrich Kraus.

Dr. Kraus looked him up and down, pumped his hand forcefully, as though he were measuring development in some secret way. Before Béla had time to open his mouth to utter some pleasantries, in an effort to ease his discomfort at being appraised by his former professor, the man motioned him briskly to a seat, and turned the full force of his dominating personality upon him. "Béla," he began, and that was surprise enough to make Béla open his eyes. Dr. Kraus had never called him by

his first name before. "Béla, I need someone to work with me—
an assistant, you understand, qualified, capable." Béla knew
that those words as used by Friedrich Kraus were not to be
taken lightly.

Béla was already hugely impressed. He could not speak.
Even if he had been able to find words Dr. Kraus gave him no
chance to use them. He was going on flatly, forcefully. "I'll
make certain that you receive the best conditions possible for
your work and experiments." Then he concluded with a
friendly, but ironic flourish. "But for the time being we won't
make you a full professor."

In spite of its friendliness, the last phrase descended on
Béla like an antitoxin. Béla had a sudden feeling that perhaps
Dr. Kraus was regretting a little that he had spoken out so
straightforwardly without first checking his ground. And yet,
Béla knew, Friedrich Kraus was not the man to make propositions he could not support. He was waiting for Béla's reply,
but Béla, overcome by the immensity of what had happened,
knowing that Dr. Kraus had never made such a proposal to a
former student before, could find no words to express the excitement it aroused. It had snatched him out of the doldrums
and placed him in the full stream of medical research activity.
It was too overwhelming for him to give a definite answer. He
managed to find his tongue sufficiently to thank his former professor and to explain that he needed a little time to consider
the matter, to settle his personal affairs, to talk things over with
his family.

He left with his head in the clouds. But it was not the end
of the surprises that were to come to him that day. He went to
talk to his young friend von Pfaundler, now a professor at the
Universitäts-Kinderklinik. He had to tell some appreciative person the great news. Ah, but Meinhard von Pfaundler had ideas
of his own. It was good to see Béla Schick back, released from
the service. He should work now somewhere where he would
be of real use. But come, he must walk with him over to Escherich. It was most important.

Dr. Theodor Escherich was the picture of genial elegance
as he greeted the two young men. He did not look much older

than they, for he was always a handsome, well proportioned man, dressed meticulously in the forefront of fashion. He had black hair and a high, so-called thinker's forehead, but the latest style of gold-framed glasses failed to subdue the perpetual twinkle in his bright blue eyes.

Béla was left breathless by the swift way in which the man invited him in. It was almost as though he had been expecting Béla, and was prepared to exercise all his organizational genius in molding his former student into the likeness he had already decided on. Pediatrics, he emphasized, was a comparatively new branch of medicine. Look how much there was to do in scientific and experimental work. Béla must turn to this field. There was no question about it. With von Pfaundler inserting periodic phrases of encouragement and agreement, Escherich spoke of his own experiences with the purpose of inspiring the young Béla Schick to a positive decision.

Born November 29, 1857 in Ansbach, Germany, and receiving his education at the universities of Würzburg, Strassburg, Kiel and Berlin, Escherich had begun his scientific activity at the beginning of what is thought of as the bacteriological era; Klebs, Löffler, Behring and Pasteur had been the foundations for his own work, and he was able to apply the discoveries of these scientists to pediatrics. He himself discovered the bacillus coli, a short gram negative motile organism found abundantly in the intestines of man. Dr. Escherich was known also as the father of the second school of thought, which maintained that bacteria were the cause of diarrhea.

The opinion of the first school was that the causes of diarrhea were pathological. This theory was set forth by the leader of that school, Herman Widerhofer (1832-1901), in a section of Gerhardt's *Handbuch der Kinderheilkunde*. He based himself on the statement of Charles Michel Billard (1800-1832) that each case of diarrhea in children was accompanied by gastritis and atrophy of the stomach, disregarding the fact that Billard himself before his death had withdrawn his assertion admitting that "there were many cases of children who were breast-fed and had diarrhea without enteritis. Often these children," he went on, "lose their color, fall into a state of progressive emaciation, and yet an autopsy performed after death shows no signs whatsoever of inflammation of the intestines."

A third school of thought maintained that the origin of the illness was not pathological, but partly bacteriological, and to a greater degree chemical. This theory resulted from the observations of an American doctor, Charles Delucena Meigs (1792-1869), who at the age of fifty-eight published a book which he entitled *Observations on Certain Diseases of Young Children,* based mainly on his own observations; his son, John Forsyth Meigs (1818-1882) expanded this work, adding deeper observations on the treatment of cyanosis neonatorum, bowel complaint, brain apoplexy, umbilical granuloma, and many other disorders.

These theories of father and son on diarrhea were followed and broadened by other experimenters: Philipp Biedert; Adalbert Czerny, a professor of Polish ancestry from Berlin; and Heinrich Finkelstein. Dr. Czerny and his adherents asserted that foods, and especially fats, are the fundamental factors in this illness.

Theodor Escherich and his assistants studied intestinal flora for many years, and his published observation on intestinal bacteria in young children at once became a classic and fundamental work. His profound knowledge of bacteriology enabled him to make pertinent observations regarding infection, therapy and immunity of diphtheria and other infectious diseases. With his arrival at the university in Graz from Munich, the Pediatric Department had become famous. He had already carried on revolutionary studies on tetany, and had published a paper stating that the basic cause of this illness was dysfunction of the parathyroids.

But no man rested less on his past successes than did Escherich. He could talk of the past, make Béla experience by proxy the excitement of his struggles and achievements, awaken the youth to the vast consideration of all that needed to be done, but he also had plans for the future. He talked of the need for institutions devoted exclusively to children. One must campaign, organize, awaken community feeling. One day . . . . Ah, his projects could inspire a heart of stone. But Béla Schick—he came back to Béla—should realize that the field was wide open for new ideas from new thinkers and new experimenters. Béla should cease his questioning at once, drop everything and come as a co-worker in his, Escherich's, clinic.

To this his friend von Pfaundler nodded emphatic agreement.

One question obsessed Béla as he started home that day, still somewhat dazed by all that had happened to him. Why should professors of three different medical departments at the university try so hard to influence him; why should they seem to feel his contribution all but indispensable? They had acted with marked spontaneity. When he had last seen them he had been a student, an unusually promising student, it was true. But now that he had graduated and had passed through six months of utterly routine practice, they were treating him as if he had already impressed the world with some startling expression of his genius. Certainly what they knew of his capabilities was wholly insufficient to explain their urgent desire for his collaboration.

It was a mystery. But the solution to the mystery was not long in revealing itself.

At the supper table that night, Béla told his family of his success among the professors. He noticed at once that while his parents received the news gravely, with a mingled awe and bafflement as they considered the disappointment for Uncle Sigismund, his brother on the other hand acted quite strangely. Whenever their eyes met, Richard's face would crinkle up into a broad grin. At other times Béla caught an expression on his face, both wise and complacent. Yet Richard made no comment. Clearly his brother knew something he was not talking about.

Immediàtely after supper, Béla suggested to Richard that they walk over to the Graz Café together; perhaps they could read the papers while having coffee and cake. Richard surprised Béla by a quick agreement, and started to talk before they had walked more than a few yards from the house.

"You know what, Béla?"

"What?"

"Everyone I've talked to has said you were a whiz in

medicine. But you're so quiet, Béla. How can one tell just what is going on inside you? I got to wondering. Maybe they're wrong. I had to do something about it."

Béla looked worried. "What did you do?"

"Set about to prove it in my own way, of course."

"But how?" Béla's anxiety made him impatient.

"The only way. By getting facts. Must have facts. Something of the scholar in me, too, I suppose . . ."

"Come on. Down to cases, down to cases," cried Béla. "Get rid of all these preliminaries. What did you do?"

"I took some notes of yours to the university." Richard looked a little sheepishly at his stunned brother.

"What!" But Béla was too horrified to go on.

"Yes," Richard went on hurriedly. "In your room they were. I came on them while you were in the service, so I couldn't ask you about them. The plan came to me right then. It seemed so good." Then as Béla still kept silent, "Look, it's too late now. It's over and done with. Forgive me, Béla, I couldn't help doing it, you know. Besides I only gave the notes to some assistant of Kraus's. Why, I don't even remember his name. He said they were interesting, and he asked me to let him show them to someone in the Kinderklinik."

Béla looked crestfallen. "Now they'll think that my family is trying to use influence to help me."

"Oh, no they won't. They don't. I told them what I'd done, that nobody knew anything about it."

"But it's still the reason why they paid so much attention to me—all three of them, I suppose. Kraus, Escherich and Meinhard von Pfaundler."

"It's the reason all right, but not because I gave them the notes. Who am I to them? It was what was in those notes that did it."

"Which notes were they?"

"I don't know. All your notes of the past years in the medical department. Extremely interesting and original is what was said about them." Richard glanced at Béla to see how he was taking it, but Béla had fallen silent again. He had a resigned look. The damage had been done; it couldn't be corrected.

When Richard showed him the notes that evening, Béla found they were those he had taken on the subject of brain sickness in infancy, together with all his personal observations. Through the next year's work as the close assistant of Professor Escherich, Béla was able to deepen and extend these observations, which became the foundation for his first scientific paper. The work was published in the *Jahrbuch für Kinderheilkunde*, No. 57, 1903.

The title of the work was long, yet quite modest and precise. Perhaps it characterized the young scholar, his methods and original thinking: "Contribution to the Knowledge of the Clinical Picture of Brain Sickness in Infancy; on the Basis of Two Cases Clinically Observed and Verified by Autopsy."

CHAPTER TEN

The Nosy Young Doctor

IN THE YEAR 1902, THEODOR ESCHERICH WAS INVITED BY THE University of Vienna to be Professor of Children's Diseases and director of the University Kinderklinik. But the eminent professor was not content to go alone; two of his assistants must go with him. One was Béla Schick. The other was Dr. Clemens von Pirquet, who also had graduated from Karl Franz University in Graz.

An honor of this sort to a former student of the "professorial genius," as they spoke of Escherich, was rare indeed. To begin with he looked upon these two young men as especially gifted students, endowed with great earnestness and determination. Yet there was still another quality they possessed, one which Escherich set great store by. This was an eternal dissatisfaction: first the refusal to accept any theory without examination; second, if the theory seemed to have been proved, an eager desire to move on into the new fields which had been opened. What does all this amount to but a persistent curiosity, a nosiness? Béla Schick was cursed with such nosiness—but a happy curse, for it pleased Escherich and ultimately made of Béla a great investigator.

Everything interested Béla. His nosiness was not limited to medical knowledge, and he could always excuse himself, if he felt the need for justification, with the axiom he accepted at this early period of his career, that "to untie the secrets of

Dr. René J. Dubos of the Rockefeller Institute for Medical Research and Dr. B. S. Oppenheimer, cardiologist, in Béla Schick's garden at Garrison, N. Y.

Johanna Pichler Schick,
Béla Schick's mother

Béla Schick's parents and sisters

Dr. Sperk
and Béla Schick
at the Scarlet Fever
Pavilion, Vienna,
Christmas, 1903

Béla Schick with child
in Scarlet Fever Pavilion,
Vienna, 1904

Béla Schick
with children
in Clinic Garden,
Vienna, 1904

Béla Schick with American medical students in front of the Diphtheria Pavilion, Vienna, where the Schick test was developed

Autographed picture of Clemens von Pirquet

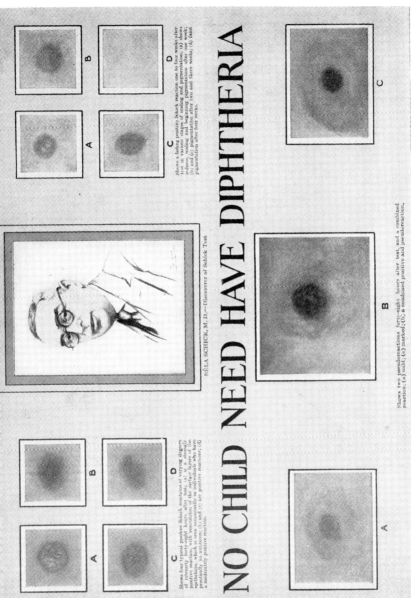

NO CHILD NEED HAVE DIPHTHERIA

BÉLA SCHICK, M.D.—Discoverer of Schick Test

Shows four typical positive Schick reactions of varying degrees of intensity forty-eight hours after test. (a) is a strongly positive reaction, with vesiculation of the upper layer of the epidermis, which is seen occasionally in individuals who have practically no antitoxin; (b) and (c) are positive reactions; (d) a moderately positive reaction.

Shows a fading positive Schick reaction one to four weeks after test in various stages of scaling and pigmentation; (a) shows redness, scaling and beginning pigmentation after one week; (b) and (c) pigmentation after two and three weeks; (d) faint pigmentation after four weeks.

Shows two pseudo-reactions forty-eight hours after test, and a combined reaction; (a) mild; (b) marked; (c) a combined positive and pseudoreaction.

Drawings showing positive Schick reactions and pseudo-reactions

A group of doctors in the garden of the Children's Clinic, Vienna, 1914. Dr. Edmund Nobel is at the extreme right; Dr. von Pirquet is in the center, with Dr. Schick at his left and Dr. Groer at his right

Doctors, nurse, and children on roof of new Children's Clinic of Vienna, August 28, 1914. Dr. Abraham Levinson of Chicago, second from left, with Dr. Schick at his right; Professor von Pirquet, third from right; Professor Groer (now in Kraków, Poland) at extreme right

Béla Schick in 1918, Vienna

Dr. Arnold
Kauffman with
Béla Schick
on S.S. Fillmore,
March, 1923

Béla Schick in 1923,
New York

Catharine Fries (later Mrs. Béla Schick) in 1915 on her graduation from Barnard College where she received BS and MS degrees

Béla Schick testing children in a New York Public School in 1923

Pediatric section of League of Nations, Geneva, Switzerland, 1925

Béla Schick with children
at Sea View Hospital

Béla and Catharine Schick (seated at extreme left) at meeting of International Child Welfare Organization, Basel, Switzerland

Béla Schick on May 1, 1928 in Washington, D. C., during a meeting
of the American Pediatric Society

Béla Schick,
Vienna, 1928

Catharine Schick,
Vienna, 1928

Béla Schick with Professor Gaston Ramon in Ramon's garden in Garches, France, September, 1929

Béla Schick with Dr. Joseph R. Morrow, Superintendent of Bergen County Hospital, New Jersey at a celebration at Bergen Pines in 1929 connected with the campaign against tuberculosis

Clemens von Pirquet's grave in Central Cemetery,
Vienna

Bust of Clemens von Pirquet in grounds of Children's Hospital, Vienna

Béla Schick with Samuel Karelitz and Sidney Blumenthal on a visit to E. R. Squibb & Sons Biological Laboratories

"Schick Alumni," May, 1933. From left to right, seated: Dr. Edward Crystel (Nutley, N. J.), Dr. Joseph Paulonis (Brooklyn), Dr. Schick, Dr. Harold Murray (Newark, N. J.). From left to right, standing: Dr. Carl Zelson and Dr. George [...] the late Dr. Maurice Ripps

Birthday party in 1935 in Children's Department of Sea View Hospital,
Staten Island, N. Y.

Béla Schick in 1938, just before receiving New York Academy gold medal

Gold medal of the New York Academy of Medicine

Cartharine Schick's parents, Carrie and Albert Fries on their golden
wedding anniversary, December 16, 1940

Béla Schick with Dr. Isaac Abt of Chicago and another member of the Society at a meeting of the American Pediatric Society, Sky Top, Pa., April, 1942.

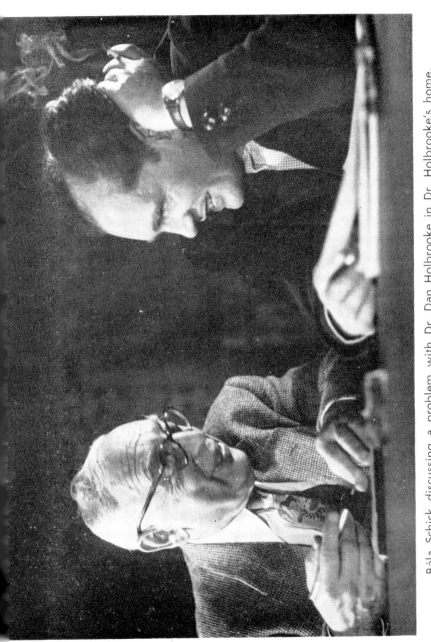

Béla Schick discussing a problem with Dr. Dan Holbrooke in Dr. Holbrooke's home, Scarsdale, N. Y., 1953

Dr. Schick with Leo Katz, the artist

Dr. and Mrs. Schick with Dr. Irvine McQuarrie, Head of Pediatric Department of University Hospital, Minneapolis, Minn., at a pediatric meeting in Mexico City, March, 1944

Dr. Schick on his 73rd birthday, July 16, 1950, en route to the International Congress

Béla Schick in his office, New York, 1950

Béla Schick with Dr. Albert Einstein and Dr. Samuel Belkin, President of Yeshiva University, on Dr. Einstein's 74th birthday, Princeton, N. J., March, 1953

medicine, one must look beyond medicine." At times this statement of his led him into difficult or amusing situations, such as the one which occurred in Graz in the summer of the year 1902, while he was preparing to leave for Vienna.

Béla was very excited over the prospect of working in Vienna. It was not only the capital of the Austro-Hungarian Empire but also the most important cultural and educational center in all Europe. Vienna was a gay city, the place of the old songs, of young beautiful women, of dances in the new waltz time of the Strausses. It was also the center of great discussions, loud discussions in the university halls and the cafés on all forms of creative endeavor, and particularly on science. Vienna and its institutions of learning had become a birthplace for original thinking in almost every sphere. Young people arrived there from all over the world to further their studies in medicine.

Béla knew that the Universitäts-Kinderklinik where he would be studying and experimenting with Escherich and Clemens von Pirquet was far more adequately equipped technically than any other comparable post in Europe.

As the time approached for Béla to leave, he made a point of visiting the homes of his friends and those of his family to bid them farewell. On his own street, Radetzky Street, lived a young lady named Hilda, who worked at Karl Franz University. Béla had walked to the university with Hilda many times. On his last day in Graz, on a sunny afternoon, he went to Hilda's house to say goodbye.

He was greeted at the door by her mother. Hilda was not at home, but most certainly Béla must stay till she got back. Béla was not unaware that the mother entertained hopes that Hilda and Béla would marry. Yes, he had a little time. He would wait, but the mother must go on with her work. He didn't want to be in the way.

The carpets were half off the floor. "We beat them yesterday," the mother explained. "But I couldn't keep them out since it started to rain. Now today is so beautiful. All that sun. I must put it to use, air them out. They are genuine Persian carpets." The emphasis was on the *Persian,* and Béla nodded politely.

As Béla sat there, wondering whether he should offer to help, the mother with the aid of a servant was carrying out the carpets. Béla began to sneeze. He tried to stifle it, without much success. The mother came back into the house, peering at him sympathetically. He must be catching a cold. She would make him some hot tea.

"No, thank you," Béla replied quickly. "It's all right, I'm not catching a cold." But the denial was difficult. He went on sneezing.

"Then why are you sneezing?" the woman pressed him impatiently. "You should look after yourself, you a doctor. Have you a temperature?"

"No, no, I haven't any temperature. I'm perfectly well." Between sneezes.

It was obvious that the mother was growing impatient with his stubbornness, and he hastily explained, "It is just the dust from your carpets "

The mother's eyes opened wide. She drew herself up straight in horror, "What did you say?"

"It is the dust from your carpets that is irritating my breathing passages," he repeated as politely as possible.

But the woman became infuriated. Hadn't she just now explained to him that she and the servant had beaten the dust out of the carpets only yesterday, and that now they were only being aired? It was as if Béla had attacked their very nationality, or as if Persian carpets could not be associated with more than a temporary veneer of dust. Béla's continued sneezing had become an accusation, and from a mild-mannered, smiling mother with a grown daughter to be married, she became a changed person. How could he, a young doctor of breeding, whose parents she knew, walk into her house with disparaging remarks that amounted to impertinence. The rugs were certainly dustless. She had watched over the servant the day before as she beat them. Everything that Béla could say to calm her only seemed to rouse her more, until she was screaming that no self-respecting girl would think of marrying him, pedantic, egotistical and critical as he was, who could think only of his nose . . . . And so on.

Béla stood still as a post, flustered, blushing and speechless, his handkerchief jammed to his nose. As the torrent of words showed no signs of abating, he bowed hastily and slipped out of the house. But the woman, hardly aware of his absence, continued to storm up and down the room defending herself as a neat housewife, only the frightened servant to take in her words. The woman's hysterical screaming voice trailed after Béla as he walked down the street.

Béla could not forget the whole incident. He was not over-sensitive, and did not take it to heart that he would never see Hilda again. But the astonishing susceptibility of his own organism to the dust from carpets started him thinking. He wanted to understand the process. He wanted to see where speculation would lead him. He would experiment. The medical profession had done little with phenomena of this kind.

It was a few years later, in Vienna, 1905, that with Clemens von Pirquet he issued a work entitled *Die Serumkran-kheit—Serum Sickness*. It was many more years before the world came to recognize the true meaning of this epochal cooperative study. It started a new branch of medicine, which these two young doctors were to call *allergy*. It contained the explanation for Béla's unusual behavior at the home of Hilda's mother, who should certainly have forgiven him, for it was not Béla's fault, it was rather the fault of his allergy.

CHAPTER ELEVEN

In Vienna

THE ROOM IN MARIANNEGASSE WAS SMALL AND DARK. THERE was an iron cot with a hard straw mattress, a table, a chair, a dresser for clothing, a basin with water for washing, and a pitcher for drinking water. The one window looked out on a sunless courtyard covered with layers of the city's dirt. The tiny lodging, hardly more attractive than a monk's cell, was the cheapest place that Béla could find in Vienna.

Béla knew from the start that he could not pay more than ten to fifteen kronen a month for a room, since his monthly stipend consisted of only fifty kronen, the fifty kronen his parents had promised to send him at the end of each month. For the first eighteen months' work with Professor Escherich, that is to say his period as a volunteer, he would get nothing. It meant full-time work at the hospital without pay, with all remaining time used for experimentation and observation, and no extra time for work that would bring in pay, such as helping the less capable students or those from foreign lands, among whom there were many Americans.

But Béla was quite content. He was far too busy to think about his sleeping quarters. His day started at six A.M. A cup of coffee or milk and a piece of bread and butter were all he allowed himself for breakfast. He would then spend fifteen to thirty minutes reading or working on the notes he had taken the day before, or preparing for the afternoon's experiments. At eight in the morning he had to report to the Scarlatina Pavilion of the Saint Anna Hospital for Children, where his good friend Clemens von Pirquet had become a resident physician. This was the oldest hospital for children in Austria. Here the morning was taken up with routine matters, diagnosis and treatment of the infectious diseases of the young patients.

Many times at noon, Clemens was able to invite Béla to lunch in the hospital dining room for resident physicians. If this was impossible, Béla had to be content with munching on a sandwich as he rode across town on the trolley at five groschen fare. At one o'clock his real work began, his true scientific labors which continued at times until after midnight.

This work in the laboratory of the Serotherapeutic Institute of the Crown Prince Rudolph Hospital, with its experiments with mice, rabbits and rats with microscopes and chemicals, so completely engrossed the young scientist that his financial problems vanished from thought. He began to forget the faithfully promised weekly letters to his parents in Graz, and his correspondence finally dwindled to a monthly acknowledgement of the receipt of fifty kronen.

As for Uncle Sigismund, the old doctor received not a line. He wrote to Janka about it, but as she could do nothing, he took decisive steps of his own. One day Béla was stunned to find Uncle Sigismund standing angrily at his door. He had come all the way to Vienna to find out for himself what was the matter.

Béla made every effort to placate him with a full account of his activities, but the truth was the old man had not come to scold, but to satisfy himself before he died that Béla was making the scientific advances he had hoped for. He must know once and for all which of the two was right—he who had urged Béla to take over the practice in Boglar, or Béla who had insisted on devoting his life to science.

As Béla talked, Dr. Telegdy began to nod his head in approval. Things seemed to be going well; there was great hope for Béla's future. Certainly he was not wasting his time.

Certainly there was no diminution in his ambition and interest. But what made him so oblivious to his surroundings? This dingy little room on Mariannegasse—could Béla do his best work in such depressing surroundings? Uncle Sigismund dug deep in his pockets. He pulled out a few hundred kronen and tried to persuade Béla to change his quarters for something more comfortable and more seemly for an aspiring young doctor.

Béla did not hesitate to take the money and hide it away. But as he did so he told Uncle Sigismund, "With this I'll be able to eat better, and because of that I'll be able to work longer. That's the most important thing. But as for my room. I don't have to change that. I'm hardly aware of it. I'm at the institute or the hospital all day and part of the night. What does it matter where I sleep when I come back almost too exhausted to undress?"

After a long and heavy silence, the old doctor smiled in acceptance of Béla's reasoning. He remained in Vienna for a few more days, forced a few more kronen into Béla's pocket, then returned to Boglar. They never saw each other again. Dr. Telegdy died towards the close of 1904. He had married late in life. His wife had borne him three children, one right after the other, in a space of three years. But one of these, a boy, was feeble-minded. Dr. Telegdy had spent a small fortune vainly trying to cure him. It left him depressed. His own health began to fail so that he had to neglect his practice, and he had no one from his family to take his place. Only Béla, but Béla was moving on to more ambitious goals. To some degree that became satisfaction for the older man.

In the meantime, Béla in his own stubborn way was making astonishing advances. His energy, his straightforwardness and sincerity gained him the affection and admiration of his fellow workers. His closest and dearest friend was Clemens von Pirquet. The two worked together on many problems. Béla's capacity for work seemed endless. He thought nothing of concentrating on several problems at the same time. After his first study on cerebral hypertrophy in childhood, he undertook two new problems. One, on the variability of diphtheria bacilli, which was brought forth in 1903 (*Wr. Klin. Wochenschrift*, No. 35). In the following year he published another work in *Wiener Klinisch-therapeutische Wochenschrift,* No. 38, based on his own observations at the Scarlatina Pavilion of the Saint Anna Hospital, and entitled "Urotropin as Prevention of Scarlatina Nephritis."

This was the beginning of a long period of toil against the infectious diphtheria and scarlet fever, a war he waged to victory "until," he said later, "I reached the lifeless end, knowing that these two dreaded diseases no longer held any secrets from the examiner, that they were completely under control. When that happened, I interested myself in something else."

In Vienna Béla had no family, no social life, no life at all beyond that which he drew from hospitals and laboratories. He lived, ate, worked and went to sleep constantly reflecting on some problem either at the institute or theoretically, within the confines of his alert mind. He observed, listened, read, experienced, examined, experimented, turning from one problem to another, always with a new approach, with an original thought.

For Béla, Vienna was not a colorful parade of the military, but a parade of convalescing children in the solarium of Saint Anna Hospital. There was no room in his life for the waltzes and the beautiful ladies of Vienna. These were supplanted by the laughing faces and bright singing of the young people under his care. This devotion, this complete consecration to medical science, and the renunciation of any private life, were no indication of abnormality. What alternative was there if his ambitions were to be fulfilled?

CHAPTER TWELVE

Pirquet and Schick

IN THE YEAR 1874, MAY 12, THREE YEARS BEFORE BÉLA'S BIRTH, Clemens von Pirquet saw the first light of day in a small country village named Hirschstetten, not far from Vienna.

At his christening he was given the somewhat pretentious name of Clemens Freiherr von Pirquet. It was a name that spoke of his background, his descent from the old French-German-Austrian lineage of landowners. His father was wealthy enough to give each of his sons a well-rounded education in the more expensive schools. His mother was a piously devout Roman Catholic, who planned and dreamed of a career in the church for Clemens. Mother of seven children, she dominated the household. Clemens was not allowed to think for himself. His food, his books, his clothing were all chosen for him by his mother, even after he had grown into a youth as tall as his father. In the last years at the Gymnasium, he was a decent and respectable young man, entirely dependent on his mother. He could not even venture forth to carry on a conversation with a girl without the express permission of his parent.

It was not surprising therefore that Clemens, upon finishing at the Gymnasium, embarked on a program of theological studies, for this was what his mother had planned. He would become a priest, perhaps in time a bishop, and—who knows?— he might end up a cardinal. For Clemens, despite his apparent lack of initiative, was remarkably clever. Whatever he was set to do he did superbly. Coming from an old Roman Catholic family with aristocratic claims, and with reliable and suitable contacts, there was no knowing how far he might go.

Go he did, but with a startling sudden fervor in a different direction. His poor mother's lifelong plans went wholly awry. Clemens dropped his studies of theology and with a blazing insistence his mother was unable to defeat he betook himself to the study of medicine. At Vienna, at Königsberg and at Graz he studied in a fine frenzy of concentration. He had to make up for lost time. The influence of his mother was drowned out in work.

After his graduation at Karl Franz in 1900, he strove for the title of professor through the successive steps of volunteer, *sekundär,* and lastly assistant. His customarily brilliant work showed up in medicine as it had done in other fields. It did not take long for the ever-watchful Theodor Escherich to discover the potential genius in this youth, as he discovered it in Béla Schick. As a result they both went to Vienna to work closely with their instructor and master, the new director of the Kinderklinik.

Through this period up to the year 1908, when Clemens received the title of Privatdozent, Clemens and Béla worked very closely together. A spontaneous friendship sprang up between them from their first meeting. It continued and increased through the years, held firm by mutual admiration, and by complementary characteristics in their make-up. Clemens was tall, thin, long-armed, and with restless eyes. He was high-strung, constantly seeking something new. Béla, on the other hand, was quiet, analytical, stubborn, precise, as his whole bearing and shortness of stature seemed to indicate.

Their first joint endeavor, as Béla described it, "Arbeiten gemeinsam mit Prof. V. Pirquet," was a paper on a theory of the incubation period, published in 1903 in No. 45 of the *Wiener Klinische Wochenschrift* under the title "Zur Theorie der Inkubationszeit." During that same year they published another work on the theory of vaccination, and right on the heels of that two others: "About the Question of Agressins" and "Oversensitivity and Accelerated Reaction."

They both spent much time experimenting on bacteriology and immunity at this time, coming to conclusions which were to be of great importance in advancing knowledge in this field. They discovered that certain animals were unusually sensitive to foreign proteins, and especially to those derived from infectious microbes. It was these intense observations and analyses which led to the beginnings of the new branch of study, that of *allergy,* as Béla and Clemens were to call it.

Their conclusions on the matter were embodied in the year 1905, as has been noted, in the book *Serum Sickness* published by Franz Deutike, which is still the basic reference book for all doctors specializing in allergies and allergic diseases. The work is divided into three sections: "Clinical Aspects of Serum Sickness," "The Reinjection," and "Theory of Serum Sickness." There is a straightforward simplicity in the statements of these earnest young doctors, a deep and original thinking which amazed the medical profession of their day. They wrote:

> An injection of the serum under the skin, creates a swelling that is smaller or larger, depending on the amount that is injected. As the serum is viscous, it takes more time to be absorbed than the exact same amount of a physiological NaCl solution. But within a span of 24 to 48 hours 200 cc. of the serum can be completely absorbed. Usually the only noticeable change is a local tenderness. The area of puncture does not show any particular reaction during the ensuing days and the general condition of health is not changed. There is no indication that an alien matter that will lead to disease is present in the system. Between 8 to 12 days after the injection, the first indications of the disease suddenly begin to manifest themselves.
>
> On infrequent occasions, prodromal symptoms can be observed a few days before the actual outbreak of the disease. The skin is sensitive to slight irritation. Around the area of injection a faint redness is noticeable. The surrounding region is somewhat reddened and tingling.

The most continual prodromal symptom is a small amount of swelling of the regional lymph nodes.

At this stage the disease itself begins with an eruption of skin manifestations, which, with rare exceptions, belong to the urticaria group. This is usually first noted at the place of puncture or injection and its surroundings. This superficial eruption disperses itself quickly over the entire body and is often perceived at the same time in symmetrical regions. If the patient scratches the itchiness to any extent, the erupting hives are surrounded by a red halo. In other cases they are partly pale. If the rash is thick they may blend into one. In that case the entire area seems to be infiltrated by edema. This edema may mar the face. The extreme itching makes the patient disquieted and miserable. . . .

From a practical point of view, the most important cases of serum sickness, because of the number of times of occurrence, are those of undeveloped character revealing only one or another symptom, usually rash and fever.

And from another section of the book:

Those who have observed serum sickness previous to this dealt mainly with the symptoms of reinjection clinically and statistically, as they had done with the first symptoms after the first injection, and did not pay particular attention to the symptoms themselves after reinjection. It was only during the course of our examination that our atention was focussed upon the prominent differences between the first injection and the reinjection, which for the most part exist in connection with the outbreak and the severity of the symptoms.

August Sch., 3½ years old, admitted 10/11/02 with scarlet fever and tbc. fungus of the right elbow joint. On 10/11 injection of 200 cc. polyvalent streptococcus serum (Paltauf). After this the patient showed no signs of fever for 8 days. On 10/20, the 10th day after injection, urticaria and fever were present, and remained several days. 10/24-11/3, no urticaria present but a 'hectic' fever, which we related to the fungus. Since then, our experience has taught us to regard the symptoms as attributable to serum sickness. We wished to determine whether the fever could again be arrested by a repetition of the serum injection. On 11/24, twenty-four days after the first injection, we injected 100 cc. of the same streptococcus serum into the skin of the abdomen. This injection was made at noon; that evening the site of the injection and the surrounding area was to a wide extent edematous and displayed a rambling redness. Erythematous Eruption was also noted on other parts of the body. The fever did not fall from its 38.4 centigrade at which it was in the first days, but rather rose to 39.7 centigrade. At first we surmised an infection but no abscess developed. Instead, the swelling of the general area of the infection returned to normal within a few days. Five to six days later urticarial and small papular eruption appeared which were quite similar to the eruption we are used to seeing in serum sickness.

The strangeness of the case was that the same child who only a month before had needed nine days to react to the serum with sickness reacted on this occasion within a few hours.

Naturally, both scientists carried on many other experiments and observations on animals and humans. But this report on the child August Sch. gives us a picture of the methods and the scrupulous care taken to be accurate.

The following is a portion from the third section of the book, "Theory of Serum Sickness."

The disparity in reactions between the first injection and the reinjection led us to the development of some theoretical explanations of this variance. It could not be caused by the antigen, that is the injected serum, as has been shown through our experiments, since there were different kinds of reaction and differently timed caused by the same serum, depending on whether it had been injected into the organism the first time or reinjected. We were able to reach the conclusion, therefore, that it was the human body which had become specifically changed, due to the initial injection of the foreign serum, and that it had acquited a new property, resulting in a swifter reaction the second time.

Now our question is what changes have occurred in the organism after being injected with the foreign serum. Biological research has revealed that particular substances are created in the injected organism. A precipitation results when these substances are brought into contact with the antigen in a test tube.

The two most significant results of our investigations, we believe to be the discovery of the immediate and accelerated reaction in serum sickness. Prior to our investigations both forms of reaction had been ignored. Other authors dealt only with the hypersensitiveness which accompanied the immediate reactivity in various antigens.

The authors conclude their book in this way:

The sooner the reaction of the organism appears, the less time has the alien intruder to multiply, the more rapidly its expansion will be restrained, and that much less will be the resulting damage to the whole organism.

However, it seems that in serum sickness it is not beneficial to have the organism react more swiftly after reinjection, because the disease will be more acute if the antibodies interact more rapidly with the antigen.

One can explain this contradiction by the fact that the insertion subcutaneously of a nonmultiplying agent rarely occurs in nature (stings by insects, snake bites). And so with serum sickness, it represents an unnatural kind of disease. For the most part, diseases are caused by the invasion of small amounts of germs that are capable of multiplication. The organism's defense mechanism is phylogenetically mobilized in accordance with this form of disease.

The acceleration in reaction is the strong benefit the organism has gained in defeating the first disease.

Immediately after the conclusion of the disease the organism is in the stage of free antibodies, and so we are able to perceive the immediate reactivity and hypersensitiveness.

This stage has only a restricted duration. The free antibodies vanish. Nevertheless, the individual is still immune. But the essence of this immunity exists no longer in a prompt reaction against the infectious germ, but rather in a hastened reproduction of antibodies.

Thus the organism is able to create a wall more swiftly around the reinfection, that is to localize it, and this is what we most clearly recognized after revaccination.

This power to localize a repeated infection is not granted because of the presence of free antibodies in the body fluid, but is due to an attribute of the cells acquired through the first disease. Here, we perceive, is an assertion of cellular immunity.

However, since a consistent account of the incubation period is not possible, it is conceivable that other kinds of cellular immunity do exist. The observations of Wassermann on the tissue's adaption to a symbiosis with originally pathogenic microorganisms, without any noticeable antibody reactions, seem to indicate a different form of immunity founded on a lack of sensitiveness.

Many diseases, such as variola, measles, varicella, rubella, are particularly marked by the fact that one victory over an invasion of the disease accords a more or less guaranteed protection for life. They are characterized by the conventional clinical trait that following an extended incubation period, one that is regular and free from the malignity of the inciting germ, the duration of the disease is very much limited.

If the organism does not yield to the disease, then it has totally vanquished the infectious agent. The latter no longer holds any threat for the organism.

The characteristic of clinical immunity for this group of diseases—as their paradigm we regard the vaccination—is not an acquired insensibility towards the infectious germ, but rather a capacity for quicker reaction.

With our studies we have tried to arouse new interest in serum sickness, and we are of the opinion

that we have demonstrated the great importance of this
disease, not only from a clinical viewpoint, but from the
standpoint of general pathology as well. Serum sickness
is the most efficient paradigm for any disease that is
attributable to an organic cause which is unable to
multiply, and is an excellent object for the investigation
of the mutations going on in the system.

All of the present allergy tests and practically everything
known today of allergic diseases is founded on the observations
on serum sickness carried out by these two young investigators.
Other problems, such as measles, vaccination, and tuberculosis,
mentioned in this book, were later investigated further by Schick
and von Pirquet together, or by each working independently.
It is not generally realized that von Pirquet is the father of all
the widely used methods of skin testing.

There were still three other problems on which they worked
cooperatively. First, on the diagnostic tuberculin reactions in
childhood. Then on the passive transmission of the intracutaneous
tuberculin reaction in guinea pigs. Finally, a study of homolog-
ical and heterological passive anaphylaxis.

Von Pirquet, not satisfied with solving problems of science
and organization, hungered for new surroundings to work in,
and opportunities to expound his theories. During the same year
(1908) that he received the title of Privatdozent at the University of Vienna, he left the country for eighteen months, having accepted the Chair of Pediatrics at the Johns Hopkins University in Baltimore, Maryland. The reason for the invitation to
the United States at this time was his fame for his successful
research on the immunological reactions following infection with
tuberculosis. On his return to Europe he became Professor of
Children's Diseases in Breslau University.

The climax of his career came in 1911, on the death of the
great Theodor Escherich. Von Pirquet was asked to take over
the professor's chair and the directorship of the Kinderklinik.

But in the meantime, while his friend was traveling all over
the world lecturing, Béla Schick was extremely busy. In 1908
he was appointed assistant to Professor Escherich at the Uni-

versity of Vienna, and while continuing his labors at the Scarlatina Pavilion of Saint Anna Hospital, he undertook an intensive scientific study of scarlet fever.

Béla attacked this problem with his usual intensity and scrupulous care, arriving at an almost complete understanding of the disease, its action and reaction. A mere listing of his publications on this subject is sufficient to indicate how deeply he explored it.

"Specific Agglutination of Streptococci Derived from Cases with Regular and Extrabuccal Primary Focus"; "Further Report on the Successful Treatment of Scarlet Fever with Specific Serum"; "Therapy of Scarlet Fever"; "Heart Symptoms in Scarlet Fever"; "Chloride Metabolism and Body Weight in Scarlet Fever"; "Post-Scarlet Fever Exanthema Elicited by Trauma"; "Post-Scarlet Fever Lymphadenitis"; "Post-Scarlet Fever Diseases"; "Infectiousness and Therapy of Post-Scarlet Fever Diseases."

Soon after these, he issued a 257-page monograph on scarlet fever. It was Béla Schick who first proved that post-scarlatinal diseases are allergic in nature. Today, this important fact is completely accepted in the medical world.

It might seem natural to assume that both Schick and von Pirquet must have made a fortune out of their discoveries, with the entire pharmaceutical business world striving for their services. The fact was that outside of the international university circles, dedicated to the development of medicine, practically no one showed any interest in their theoretical works. Not one medical magazine or publication offered them a penny for their writings.

As Béla said later, recalling these days of his youth, "It was a case of twelve hours a day without letup, seven days a week, if anything worthwhile was to be done, that is if the urge to solve some medical problem was to be gratified." His friend Clemens was more fortunate. Receiving money from his family, he did not have to worry about outside work for a living, and was in the happy position of being able to devote all his time to scientific investigation. As for Béla, he struggled along on his fifty crowns a month for the first year and a half of his stay in

Vienna. Then the supply stopped, for the simple reason that his parents could no longer spare it.

The years 1904 to 1908 were scientifically fruitful for him but financially difficult; nevertheless he had to keep going. He continued working at the Kinderklinik, receiving twenty-five crowns a month with one meal a day. If there was a piece of meat in this one meal he would save it for his supper, which usually consisted of the treasured morsel, plus a slice of bread and some coffee.

But Béla felt no resentment and no self-pity. He seemed able to drown out any feeling of undernourishment by increased concentration on his medical problems, particularly relating to diphtheria. The higher he climbed the harder it became to keep going. With the title of Assistent der Universitäts-Kinderklinik, he lost the twenty-five crowns a month. At the same time the cost of living in Vienna was going up. Something drastic had to be done. He calculated that he needed at least one hundred crowns a month for bare subsistence.

Languages had always come easily to Béla. He knew Latin and French, and now with a few months of study he mastered English. Then he let it be known that he was ready to give private courses in theory and laboratory procedures for English-speaking students, who had been attracted by the fame of Escherich from all parts of Great Britain and the United States. For the most part these students came from wealthy families. Because of the difficulties of the language, or because of inadequate abilities, they were glad to get private lessons from the young scholar. They paid well and promptly.

Béla found this work easy, but it consumed a great deal of time, time that was so precious to him. His mind was straining forward to ever greater scientific work. There seemed to him so many problems to be probed, investigated, untangled.

CHAPTER THIRTEEN

Diphtheria

BÉLA SCHICK HAD A WAY WITH HIM DURING WORK—AN ASSURED, unruffled, efficient manner, at the same time straightforward and considerate. He made friends all around him, wherever he was and whatever he was doing. Everyone liked his constant cordiality, particularly the nurses who thought themselves lucky if they could arrange to be on duty during Dr. Schick's rounds at the hospital or the clinic. He never misused his authority, but behaved as if he were unaware of his own unusual accomplishments.

Once in awhile, Béla would receive the suggestion from one of the more strait-laced of his fellow doctors that it was important for a man of his position to set an example, meaning that he should maintain a certain superior distance as a doctor and a scientist and not have too much to do with the hospital staff.

It was not in Béla's nature to take offense, but a good-natured smile would play over his ample lips. "You know," he would say, "I realize so well both my limitations and my contributions to medicine." Such reply was a bit difficult for his colleague to handle, and if Béla felt expansive he would continue in a philosophical tone: "All of us admire this marvelous palace of nature that is the human body. I suppose it could be likened to a building with many windows, millions of them. Everybody can peer in and try to find out what is happening inside. But there is so very much to see, and we don't live long enough to see everything. So, we must resign ourselves to being able to look through only a few of those windows. And I think we should be extremely happy if we are able to understand some minute part of this beautiful house of nature. Don't you think then that this happiness must, of necessity, be combined with modesty."

This was not a pose with Béla. It was his constant attitude towards life.

On his birthday in 1911, he received a present from the nurses of the children's clinic, a small, brightly wrapped package. He opened it to find a box of visiting cards with his name:

PROFESSOR DR. BÉLA SCHICK

1. ASSISTENT DER UNIVERSITÄTS-KINDERKLINIK

Wien, IX., Lazarettgasse 14

Béla was embarrassed. He thought the nurses knew that he possessed no visiting cards like his more prosperous colleagues, and possibly too they were aware of how he lived: his miserable sleeping quarters and the hunger always about to press too hard. Nevertheless, Béla concealed his feelings as he began to express his thanks to the group of nurses who had gathered around him, and he found himself making a little speech to his delighted audience.

"In spite of all our adversities," he told them, "it appears to me that none of us fully realize how much good fortune we actually have in our lives. It is quite true that we must work hard, and have to make sacrifices in order to succeed. But experience teaches us that the harder we work on our life's task, the greater is our satisfaction as we approach the goal . . . ."

After a brief pause, as though reflecting, he added: "I am especially grateful to my teachers, Friedrich Kraus and Theodor Escherich, and to my friend, von Pirquet . . . ."

The visiting cards were to become useless in a short while, for it was in 1912 that Béla was named to be the Privatdozent of Children's Diseases of the University of Vienna. About this time and lasting for a period of several years occurred his most intense investigations into diphtheria. Béla found nothing in life as interesting as the diphtheria bacillus, and his writings on various aspects of this disease had a way of beginning in an extremely free and open manner. It was his way of encouraging his newly indoctrinated students, luring them on with a smooth and easy manner into the deeper, the more important, the more technical problems. A quote seems worth-while, to show how a learned scholar in those days could speak vitally and clearly on an advanced and difficult subject.

In the words of Louis Pasteur, "It is within the power of civilized man to cause infectious diseases to disappear from the earth." Even though the attainment of this ideal in its entirety may still be very far removed, its full realization is by no means Utopian as far as diphtheria is concerned. It is wholly possible to cause this particular infectious disease to disappear entirely from the earth because we now possess an easy and effective method of immunizing children against diphtheria.

The striking observation was made over an extended period of time that diphtheria occurs mostly in young children and is relatively rare among adults. After Klebs and Löffler discovered the diphtheria bacillus and Emil von Behring noted the fact that it was the toxin produced by this bacillus which caused the disease, he made the further discovery that it was possible to produce an antitoxin in animals, namely horses. This antitoxin was found to accumulate mostly in watery parts of the blood-serum. The serum counteracts the poisonous effect of the toxin, and is useful in helping the child fight off the life-endangering action of the diphtheria bacillus.

It was found too that human beings produce such counteracting substances after they have combated the disease. It was further discovered that of 100 adults about 85 had such substance in their serum, even though they did not remember having suffered from diphtheria. It was established therefore that adults are protected against diphtheria by the possession of such antibodies. This then is the answer to the riddle of why adults as a rule do not become infected with diphtheria.

Dr. Schick concluded his observations with these words:

It was extremely interesting to note that mothers of newborn children, being adults and therefore usually immune to diphtheria, transmit this protection to their newborn children. In the newborn child we find antibodies in the same frequency as in adults. This protection derived from the mother is gradually lost during the first year of life, so that almost every child at the end of its first year is no longer protected against the dangerous diphtheria.

Delicately Béla Schick would approach the more profound implications of the problem. Yet he did not smother his ideas by circumlocutions; the pure line of his basic thought and purpose was never obscured. It was precisely this quality in his writings and dissertations that made him popular among students. When he addressed a group of people he was no orator. His manner was quiet, warm, confiding. He seemed to break down the barrier between speaker and listener.

In his writings Béla never failed to applaud the works of his predecessors, to praise his collaborators, no matter how minute the assistance might have been. He customarily ranked himself last. The attack on medical problems was to him an essentially cooperative venture, an attitude astonishing in the medical world where strong professional jealousy is common.

Béla explored diphtheria from many sides, never content to rest on what he had already discerned. He constantly enriched his knowledge and drew in an increasing number of workers. The summit of his success against the disease came with the utilization of the Schick test, which was announced to the whole world in the year 1913.

Before that momentous date, he had published eight works on various aspects of diphtheria in Austrian and German medical journals and other periodicals. The first work in this category was a study concerning the diphtheria antitoxin content of human serum. The second dealt with the diphtheria antitoxin content of the serum of children suffering from diphtheria and measles.

Soon after, other works appeared: "Quantitative Determinations of the Curve of Resorption of Diphtheria Antitoxin Subcutaneously Injected by Intracutaneous Method"; next a publication concerning immunity against diphtheria; then the "Determination of the Content of Diphtheria Antitoxin by Intracutaneous Testing." Three discussions followed under the general title "Cutaneous Inoculation with Diphtheria Toxin," in which he wrote about the results of testing children and guinea pigs by injection of diphtheria toxin. Béla also published a large book on the treatment of diphtheria in children, and in the very same year, 1913, his series of lectures on the treatment of diphtheria by serum—lectures which he had delivered in Berlin—were enthusiastically received at the nation-wide Convention of German Microbiologists, and subsequently before the United German Biologists and Physicians.

He wrote in the same year a short but highly significant article in the *Muenchener Medizinische Wochenschrift:* "The Skin Reaction with Diphtheria Toxin on Human Beings as a Test Preceding the Prophylactic Injection of Diphtheria Serum." In order to understand the scientific implications of the Schick test it is worth-while to quote from this article, as translated from the German by Béla himself.

> The investigations of Loos, Karasawa and Schick, and others, show that children suffering with diphtheria, examined before the injection of antitoxin, do not possess diphtheria antitoxin in their serum. The examination of such children in the last years by Busacchi, Kassowitz and myself give the same result.
>
> The prophylactic injection of diphtheria antitoxin should supply the missing antitoxin. According to the investigations of Wassermann, Fischl, Groer and Kassowitz, and Kleinschmidt, many individuals possess antitoxin in their serum without having shown during their lives

any symptoms of diphtheria. Eighty per cent of newborn babies show such antibodies, of adults up to 90 per cent and of children 50 to 60 per cent (Magyar and Schick). One could, therefore, omit the injection of antitoxin in many instances if there existed a method of determining the presence of antitoxin in the serum.

The old methods are not satisfactory. Roemer's method of testing the guinea pig intracutaneously is an important step forward, but it is too complicated and too expensive, as guinea pigs have to be used; Lowenstein, Michiels and Schick could prove that intracutaneous injection of minimal amounts of diphtheria toxin produces a specific inflammatory reaction at the site of the injection.

For this injection a regular record syringe of 1 cc. with ten partitions is needed. The most important part is the needle. The latter must be very thin and its point very short so that after introduction of the needle into the uppermost layer of the skin the opening of the needle pointing upward is covered as easily as possible. The amount of injected fluid should be 1 cc. of a toxin solution, the strength of which must be determined for each batch of toxin. As a rule, the effective dose is equal to 1/50th of a single lethal dose for a 250 gram guinea pig. . . . If the injection is made correctly a white wheal with punctuations is seen immediately.

The reaction developing at the site of the injection of the toxin very much resembles in the first 24 to 38 hours a positive tuberculin reaction. Four to 8 hours after the disappearance of the traumatic reactions, gradually increasing redness and infiltration (10 to 25 mm. diameter) develop. Usually the maximum is reached after 48 hours; the reaction lessens under pigmentation and slight desquamation. But the quality of the redness is different from the tuberculin reaction. The redness is brighter. In case of a great intensity the inflammatory reaction increases, particularly in the center. The skin becomes blistered, gelatinous and shrivelled. Pigmentation and desquamation follow. I did not encounter more intensive reactions. The necrosis described by Bingel is due to the enormous dose of diphtheria toxin. Frequently a brighter red halo develops around the central infiltration within 24 to 36 hours. This halo disappears in the following 24 to 36 hours without leaving any pigmentation. Later on, only the central reaction is visible by its pigmentation, and the size of the original reaction may be measured by the diameter of the pigmented area of the skin.

The negative result of the rest proves the presence, in the serum, of protective antibodies against diphtheria toxin in an amount sufficient for prophylaxis. The positive result of the test does not prove with certainty the lack of such antibodies, because some individuals, children and adults, show inflammatory reactions at the site of the injection, although antibodies may be present in the serum. Although such inflammatory reactions are not the effect of the diphtheria toxin proper, but are possibly an hyperergic reaction to protein substances present in the diphtheria solution, it is sometimes difficult to differentiate such "pseudo-reactions" from the original reaction due to the diphtheria toxin proper. On account of these exceptions, decisive conclusion about the presence of antibodies should be drawn only if the test is negative.

I mentioned before that the presence of antibodies in the serum is incompatible with the presence of a fresh diphtheria disease. So we may expect that children suffering with diphtheria react positively to the test if this test is applied before the injection of diphtheria antitoxin. This is always the case. A negative test in doubtful cases of diphtheria speaks against diphtheria.

An exception exists in case of malignant diphtheria (Busacchi, Kassowitz, Schick). Also, extremely cachetic individuals are unable to react positively to diphtheria toxin. Von Groer and Kassowitz found negative reactions in 10 per cent of newborns, in spite of the absence of antitoxin, which may be explained by a lowered ability of the skin of the newborn to react.

I have previously pointed out that the test with diphtheria toxin reveals susceptibility to diphtheria. If the testing should lead to a reduction of prophylactic serum treatment against diphtheria, we must be able to prove that the percentage of negative reactors is large enough. Information can be achieved by a statistical survey of the results of the test arranged in age groups.

These figures, taken from the investigation of Magyar, Michiels and Schick, and von Groer and Kassowitz, are as follows:

	Total	+	−		
Newborn	291	16	275	=	93%
1 year	42	18	24	=	57%
2-5 years	150	95	55	=	37%
5-15 years	264	131	133	=	50%

Newborns, who possess antitoxin in 84 per cent and show a negative test in 93 per cent, need no prophylactic treatment in most cases. . . .

Our experience is that the frequency of negative tests diminishes from the second month of life and reaches about 50 per cent in the first year. In this period 50 per cent of the children need no prophylactic treatment. In the next period 40 per cent show negative reactions. Towards the end of childhood again 50 per cent is reached. After that the number of negative reactions probably increases further. We see that during childhood and even in the period between two and five years a considerable number of individuals need no prophylactic injection with serum.

It could be stated that the state of immunity of an individual may change, especially under the influence of certain diseases (influenza, measles, etc.). As far as measles is concerned, Karasawa and Schick were not able to find any change. But it should be admitted that other diseases may have such an influence. The reaction remains unchanged within four weeks. In order not to overlook the loss of antibodies, it may be advisable to repeat the test in institutions once every month in case danger of infection persists. For institutions such as hospitals, military barracks and boarding houses for children, testing has a practical value.

Our procedure is the following: If a case of diphtheria develops, all persons are tested with diphtheria toxin. Twenty-four to 48 hours later the test is read. The positive reactors are injected with serum; the negative reactors are not. Thus we spare many individuals the injection and the sensitization with horse serum. This is also an economic saving, as the use of large amounts of diphtheria serum is expensive.

To complete the story, it must be added that in 1908 Dr. Schick started work on his test by using the scratch method in order to bring diphtheria toxin into the skin. This procedure gave satisfactory results, but for practical purposes Dr. Schick replaced it by the method of intracutaneous injection of diphtheria toxin. And it was this method that was made known by him in 1913 and accepted by medical circles.

The First World War prevented the use of the Schick test on a wider scale in Europe, but in the United States, as early as 1914, Dr. William H. Park, noted bacteriologist, recognized the importance of the Schick discovery in combatting diphtheria, and from New York City he started a wide campaign for its use.

CHAPTER FOURTEEN

Assistant of the Clinic

FOR THE MEDICAL WORLD, FOR THE VIENNA STUDENTS AND THE thousands of children who had grown to know and worship Dr. Theodor Escherich, and indeed for Viennese society as a whole, since there was no one more popular with romantic young ladies of the day, it was a deep tragedy when the twinkling blue eyes behind their gold-framed glasses, the distinguished forehead and trim goatee of the brilliant Director of the Pediatric Clinic were seen no more in the city.

Dr. Escherich died in 1911, cut short in the prime of life with half of his work still in the stages of planning.

He had no equal in his time, either as a teacher and scholar, or as an organizer. With his assistants and medical cohorts he dedicated himself to the establishment of a legendary method of learning in Vienna which attracted students from all over the world. In 1905 the American Pediatric Society unanimously elected him an Honorary Life Member.

Escherich's organizational ability was apparently motivated by his profound love of children, for whom he organized various types of community medical institutions. The protection and care of infants took up most of his last years. In addition to his scientific work and teaching, he devoted his energies to organizing, founding and building a worthwhile medical facility for children. Vienna is greatly indebted to him for the State Institute For the Care of Mothers and Infants.

The old Pediatric Clinic was not good enough, he reasoned, for the most comprehensive scientific studies. He turned his attention to organizing support for a new clinic, and he lived just long enough to see the new building going up.

Only the bare walls shone in their nakedness when the directorship of the clinic was assumed by Clemens von Pirquet and his assistant Béla Schick, both conscious of the honor that was theirs to follow in the footsteps of their dear professor.

At Clemens' suggestion the supervision of interior arrangements was taken over by Béla. The laboratories, the operating rooms, the patients' rooms, the wards, kitchens, and so on—these had to be equipped and distributed in a way that would be of maximum service to the doctors in caring for their patients. Béla took over the whole of this organizational problem.

When the new clinic was opened it was seen to be a model of efficient cooperation. Director von Pirquet, his collaborator Béla Schick, and their assistant doctors—E. Nobel, K. Kassowitz, H. Wimberger, W. König, E. Mayrhofer, and R. Wagner—found they could work as they had never been able to work before. Here in this clinic was created a closely knit cooperative endeavor among the doctors and the nursing staff, their mutual aim being the more exact and intelligent care of patients. Even the kitchen was regarded by both doctors and nurses as a laboratory, faced with the problem of extracting the best and most suitable nutrition, whatever was needed for the recovery of children of all ages and in all stages of ill health.

The N.E.M. system was established. This meant Nutrition Element Milk, and was based on the idea of using the sitting height of a child instead of his weight as an index of his food requirements. As a measure of nutritive value they used one N.E.M. unit, which equals the food value of 1 cc. of milk. It had the value of 0.67 calories. In this system the nutritional value of food is assessed against a standard which can be handled accurately and easily and can be naturally seen. 100 N.E.M.s is equivalent to 100 cc. of milk, or 1 hectonem.

For accurate measurements, special utensils were hung in

the kitchen, including cylinders on which were marked singular N.E.M. units. If a physician prescribed a certain number of calories, even the most inexperienced nurse was able to measure off these calories, bearing in mind that one N.E.M. corresponded to 0.67 calories.

Using the N.E.M. system, it was easy to control the nutrition of the newborn and older children, giving them exactly the portions demanded or needed by their bodies of protein, fat and carbohydrate, accurately and satisfactorily measured according to age, weight and condition of health. There was no longer the problem of some youngsters overeating and others getting too little nourishment, and in the long run the system was found to cut down the amount of food needed for the clinic. The system had its most extensive application when after the First World War in Vienna alone, under the direction of von Pirquet and Schick, over 400,000 children were fed daily.

Naturally, before this system can be applied, it is necessary to examine the child medically in order to ascertain his general well-being and nutritional state. Thereupon each child receives a certain amount of nourishment of suitable N.E.M., according to need and age. It would be valuable to test this system on a larger scale under normal conditions, for example, in schools and in other public institutions where great amounts and varieties of food are distributed.

Béla Schick now went on to enlarge the N.E.M. system to apply it to the nourishment of premature births. He himself had been born prematurely. He had survived because of the good work of Uncle Sigismund. Nevertheless, because of certain difficulties involved in nourishing prematurely born infants, a great number of them died.

It was a problem which concerned Béla considerably. He worked until he was able to solve it. Here is his own statement on the matter:

A pressing indication for concentration of food value is found in prematurely born infants. One of the most important factors in keeping a premature child alive is nourishment. All of us are aware of how difficult this is. Often we need dropper-spoon and even tube feeding. The food requirement per kilogram is quite high, and the smaller and weaker the infant, the more difficult it is to feed such large quantities. In such cases I attempted to increase the caloric value of breast milk by adding cane sugar or dextri-maltose. To 100 cc. of breast milk (equivalent to 68 calories) we used to add 17 grams of sugar (representing 100 N.E.M.), thus increasing the caloric value to 100 per cent. And because of that, from 33 to 50 per cent less of sweetened human milk than pure human milk could be fed, with the same caloric value.

It was interesting to note that the child liked the sweetened breast milk. The general condition was good. In the first three or four days of life we tried to force only enough food value to prevent loss of weight. Later on, by increasing the intake, we succeeded in obtaining a gain in weight. Contrary to all theories, we did not perceive any symptoms of gastrointestinal disorders. Frequently the children were constipated, or had stools like in starvation, apparently because the absorption of foodstuffs was so complete.

We realized from the start that both mixtures were deficient in protein and salt, and not fit substitutes for unchanged human milk for any length of time. A mixture poor in such important building elements as protein and salt could be given only about two or three weeks. But this time usually suffices in feeding a premature child, as the first days of its life are the critical ones. If, after two or three weeks, the child has learned to take larger quantities, we may change the sweetened to plain breast milk. Where breast milk was absent or scarce, we tried whole cows' milk with the same percentage of additional sugar, either mixed with sweetened breast milk or alone.

This new clinic for children was also the incubator for yet another experiment, later followed in many parts of the world. This was the so-called Cubicles for Infants. It began with the building of a single bed for newborn infants who needed complete isolation because of a precarious state of health. This bed was separated from the others by high glass walls, one of which could be lifted like a window, making it possible to feed and tend the baby, change its clothing and fix its bed. The infant was cared for effectively and efficiently, in an isolated, peaceful atmosphere and in a temperature evenly controlled.

Both Clemens and Béla watched results closely. It was seen that such isolated infants recovered more quickly than those tended in the usual way in the ward. They decided therefore with the aid of the technical engineer Ehmann to build a unit of six small beds, separated one from the other by high glass walls. Each of these cubicles could be opened by the raising of one wall. All therapeutic measures, injections and infusions, as well as all nursing needs were taken care of in this manner. Through the open space hands were thrust in and the work accomplished while the face of the nurse or doctor remained behind the glass. The child could also be observed from the outside without contact, thus minimizing the danger of infection.

Infants aged up to eight months were kept in the cubicles and without exception fared better than those in the ward.

Years later Béla, in cooperation with Dr. Samuel Karelitz, was instrumental in introducing similar cubicles into the Pediatric Department of Mount Sinai Hospital in New York. These were impressive glass-enclosed rooms on wheels, which could be drawn into the rays of sunshine, or even to the outdoor porches. Thus American babies too shared the benefits of this experiment by the thoughtful, inventive and ingenious Béla Schick.

CHAPTER FIFTEEN

His War

THE AUSTRO-HUNGARIAN EMPIRE WAS DRAWING SWIFTLY TO ITS END. The great powers on the Continent could no longer appease their differences by dividing, enslaving the little people. They must needs turn and rend each other. The disquieted little people themselves must be appeased by an even greater show of glory than the pomp a despotic court could provide. Thus blindly unaware of its own doom, the empire of the great Franz Josef drew its grandiose but antiquated sword, and the people who had become used to festivity thought it all like a carnival, with the donning of a soldier's uniform the most important act of all.

Even those who wanted none of it were drawn in. Béla Schick had his own war, the only war he wished to fight—the war against infectious diseases. But with life changing all about him, Béla became increasingly aware that he could not remain isolated. His own world was being invaded. Franz Josef needed medical men, for now the care and healing of children was less important to the Emperor than the care of his army.

In 1914 there were twenty doctors working in the Kinderklinik. This number began to dwindle. Medical students began to melt away at an equal rate. Everything was swallowed up by the machinery of war. It became more and more difficult to obtain the necessary medical supplies. Understaffed and undersupplied, the clinic struggled on until just two doctors remained: Clemens von Pirquet, the director, and his assistant Béla Schick. Both began to wonder when their turn would come to be pulled into the army.

Béla especially wondered, for he was younger than his friend, and he bore the rank of Captain of the Reserves of the Medical Division. As he walked through the streets to and from the clinic, he became more and more depressed. The city had changed. It would never be the same again. Who heard the strains of the waltz any more? Now it was the military march. The people seemed to be able to work themselves into a frenzy of excitement over the frequent sound of clattering military boots, the rattle of military carriers and gun-carriages. As yet this excitement held no tinge of fear. The people relished the war. Those who dared show any inclination to dislike or distrust it were quickly condemned, and even to walk through the streets appearing unconcerned was sufficient to arouse suspicious frowns. Béla began to be aware that these frowns were directed upon him, as upon all the younger ununiformed men.

Much as Béla wanted to ignore these looks, he found himself becoming more and more sensitive. On the defensive, he began studying the faces of all his acquaintances to try to read their feelings toward him. It even seemed to Béla that his good friend Clemens had been gazing at him with that same alienated, suspicious expression. What were the nurses thinking? he wondered. And he even wondered about the children. There was surely a difference in their behavior towards him. He loved the children. Every morning he would go to his young patients, talk to them, play with them, entertain them. Now he felt they had become influenced in some way. There was an unfamiliar restraint. Were they too being taught to frown upon him for remaining a civilian?

Unable to stand it any longer, he came to a quick decision. He chose a Wednesday, the day when there was least to do at the Kinderklinik. He sneaked out for an entire afternoon. It took him over two hours to clean his captain's uniform, which he had last worn a full fourteen years ago, and he had to move the buttons a little to make it a comfortable fit. Even so he felt somewhat foolish and dated, not knowing whether this type of uniform was now being worn. It took courage for him to walk through the streets like that, but he was determined to go through with it. He would register for active service in the Medical Division. He was conscious of looks from the passers-by, and it angered him that he could not tell whether their smiles meant approval or ridicule. Still more was he angered that he cared about their thoughts at all. Far from feeling proud or brave about his action, he felt guilty.

On arrival at the recruiting office he was in no mood to accept the statement of the military authorities that they would have to search for documents. He would have to wait while they searched. How long? They told him a matter of thirty minutes. But thirty minutes stretched out to an hour, an hour and a half, two hours. He paced the floor in complete dejection. This aimless waiting seemed to symbolize for him the frustration of his whole life—so much to do that was important, so little time to do it in, and so much time wasted, wasted, like this, doing something that had no meaning to him, keeping him from his true and important duties . . . .

Then they called him. They could find no record of a Captain Béla Schick. They would have to continue the search further. It might take days. They would notify him.

Béla greeted this news with vast relief. His one request was that they would certify in writing that he had presented himself at the Army Recruiting Office. Then without losing another moment he hastened back to his duties at the Kinderklinik. He was in such a hurry to get back to work, to make up for all the lost time, that he all but forgot how he was dressed. At the clinic he was greeted with cries of dismay. Béla remembered the uniform, and tried to look a little more military, but at the same time he was puzzled by the crestfallen looks of the nurses. It was the children who opened his eyes to the truth of the matter, for at the first glimpse of him they began to cry, sob, whimper and wail. They thought Béla was going away to the war, that they would never see him again. The nurses were distressed. The clinic would never be the same without Béla there, and who would play the piano for them in their leisure hours? Even Clemens had tears welling in his eyes.

So that was what had concerned them! It was fear that he might go to war, not as he imagined, condemnation. He pulled out the note from the recruiting office which stated that his documents could not be found, and that time was needed before he could be considered for the army.

Clemens laughed heartily, and the note was passed around in a general atmosphere of relief. "Let them take as long as they want," said Clemens. "May they never find the documents. That would be better still. It's here you are wanted, Béla. And what would the children do if they didn't find you around? As for the nurses, why they might even go after you."

The work at the Kinderklinik became even more pressing as the war continued. In addition to doing the work of twenty doctors at the clinic itself, Béla and Clemens organized special centers throughout the city for the medical care and nutrition of the children, who from the beginning of hostilities had come into their charge.

A special concern of Béla Schick was Elsa, a girl of seven, who had infantile paralysis. Béla tended Elsa every day, partly because she was a homeless orphan, partly because poliomyelitis was a sickness concerning which little was known. Béla recalled that during the early days of his medical career in Graz he had seen a similar case, a child suffering from the dread disease of inflammation of the gray matter of the spinal cord. At that time Béla, seeing that his young patient was unable to move his right hand, had prepared special coordinative gymnastics for the entire body with most consideration given the attacked muscles, to which he also applied hot compresses and applications. These hot applications and the intensive gymnastics of the arms and legs had brought the child partially back to normal.

With the same method, Béla treated little Elsa in Vienna and achieved some degree of benefit. This was many years before the Kenny treatment became so well known to the medical world, a treatment closely resembling that used by Béla in the years 1900 to 1915.

Another extra burden on Béla's shoulders at this time resulted from a friendship with the well-known August Reuss, author of a significant book, *Diseases of the Newborn*, and pediatrician at the Schauta Clinic. With the war he had been drafted into the armed forces, and had asked Béla to take over his practice. It was a great honor, for Dr. Reuss was recognized throughout the world as a pioneer in observation of the pathology and physiology of the newborn. The private Viennese clinics, Schauta and Peham, were the first institutions in the world where obstetricians worked hand in hand with pediatricians. They introduced the method whereby a newborn child was never removed from the side of its mother and slept in its own crib attached to the mother's bed. The mother nursed the child from her breast starting the very first day, and, if able, she was urged to care for the needs of her infant, washing and dressing it, from that first day.

This method was a great advance in the organization of maternity and newborn service in Vienna, where the death rate among newborns was already the lowest in the entire world. One of the major causes of success was the fact that infants were not packed into over-filled nurseries, for even the best organized and most scrupulously cleaned nurseries are not immune to the possibilities of diarrhea or other infections.

Both August Reuss and Béla Schick agreed on these matters. They urged that babies be born at home whenever possible, always of course under competent medical care and provided there were no foreseen complications. In the home, germs are less virulent and danger of infection can be minimized. If complications make this impossible the next best thing, they agreed, was the hospital where mother and child remain in the same room.

These methods, popularly called "rooming in," which were advocated by Reuss and Schick fifty years ago, are now accepted by the medical profession as best both physically and psychologically. But it has not been an easy acceptance, and time is still needed to effect the radical changes such acceptance involves. Much remains to be done, even in so progressive a country as the United States. In line with this it is worth quoting a statement made by Béla Schick in a discussion with the noted American physician, Dr. Joseph Brennemann, at the conference of American pediatricians in August, 1931.

He spoke thus of conditions in the nurseries of the maternity wards of New York hospitals twenty-three years ago:

> The newborn children 'lie like loaves of bread one near to the other and in *étages*.' A physician told me that he visited such a nursery and saw a child's vomitus on his bedding. He asked the nurse whether this child had vomited. The nurse said, 'No, not this child, but the child above him.' Once I visited a nursery where thirty-four children were crowded in a relatively small room and only four nurses were on duty. There were not even enough cribs available, and drawers of the desks were used to put the infants in. As I left the room another newborn was brought in. Where it was placed I do not know. If a determination of the consumption of oxygen and production of carbon dioxide would have been made in these rooms, where nurses and physicians added to the overcrowding, one would have found the situation to have been worse than in the slums.

As a result of this overcrowding there were epidemics of diarrhea and other illnesses which usually had an extremely high mortality, reaching as high as eighty per cent, as happened in one medical institution in New York, and this almost ten years after the publication of Dr. Schick's remarks.

CHAPTER SIXTEEN

The "Extraordinary" Professor

"EVIL EVENTS FROM EVIL CAUSES SPRING," SAID ARISTOPHANES OVER two thousand years ago. It applies well to the conditions prevalent in Vienna and throughout the whole of Europe during the First World War. With each new day there was more hunger, less bread; more sick and maimed, less doctors and medicines; more crime, less honesty; and more children, abandoned children of all ages, wandering about the streets miserably begging for some means of staying alive. Everything seemed evil and perverse.

The Austro-Hungarian Empire was falling apart, and with it the political, economic and social system of the old monarchic regime. More and more people were coming to recognize the fact. New political ideas were being formulated, and pressed, while a general mood of uneasiness seized upon even the most sheltered citizens. The people were growing accustomed to living from day to day, never knowing and at last not troubling their minds with what the next day would bring. Béla Schick was aware of these things, suffering the same material hardships, but with the tremendous weight of duty on his shoulders and his deep sense of responsibility, he fought against sliding back into lassitude and dejection.

Certain unsolved problems of tuberculosis in children plagued him, as did the methods of treating and healing the disease. It was a sickness that increaséd a great deal during wartime. Meanwhile, he was making clinical observations on the so-called allergic diseases: asthma, eczema, vasorhinitis, urticaria, migraine, a certain form of epilepsy. He was also studying idiosyncrasies to certain foods and drugs, or as they are better known, chemical allergies, and he accompanied this with the building of fundamental observations on icterus neonatorum or the so-called physiological jaundice in the newborn. A few years later, Béla was the first to call attention to the role of the placenta in this process.

It took almost thirty years for the rest of the medical world to recognize the significance of his findings and observations. Among American scientists, Dr. A. A. Weech, Professor of Pediatrics at the College of Medicine, University of Cincinnati, proved and confirmed these observations. He delivered a lecture in New York, in the Blumenthal Auditorium, May 6, 1946, in which he said of Béla:

> His name must be placed alongside those of Ylppö and Hirsch, the pioneers in the study of neonatal jaundice. To Béla Schick belongs the credit for an observation which not only called attention to the role of the placenta in the process but also stimulated others to add new items of knowledge. The presence of a green ring in the placenta of the dog led Schick to guess that this organ must play an active part in catabolizing maternal hemoglobin. His histological preparations demonstrated greater activity of this type in premature than in term infants, a finding which correlates with the known greater susceptibility of premature infants to icterus neonatorum. At the direct instigation of Schick, Wagner studied the iron content of placentas and found that the placentas of premature infants contain more iron than do those of term infants. This work in turn stimulated still another study, one by Wiliamson. . . .

And so continued the chain of discoveries, all beginning with Béla's work during those trying years in Vienna.

Béla later published a work on icterus neonatorum as a result of blood destruction in mothers, "Der Icterus Neonatorum eine Folge des Abbaues Mütterlichen Blutes."

While these and similar scientific discoveries by Béla Schick are discussed only in medical circles even today, his discoveries concerning the physiological nail-line of the newborn have been widely discussed by all people, and had particularly wide application during the period of the First World War. The physiological nail-line of the newborn is a transversal wall-like line which is moved forward to the nail end. Legal medicine, or as it is also called medical jurisprudence throughout the world has adopted this theory. The matter is as straight and as simple as war is sad and tragic. Thus: if a few-weeks-old or a few-months-old infant is found dead, how is one to go about determining its age? Béla claimed that a child around 28 to 30 days old has a physiological nail-line of half a millimeter. In 40 days the line is one millimeter, in 50 days it becomes two millimeters, in 60 days—three, in 70 days—four, in 80—five, and in the ninetieth day of life, or in a three-month-old child, the physiological nail-line measures six millimeters.

There are probably few scientific questions in pediatrics that this scientist has not tried to solve. At times his observations went far beyond the realm of pediatrics, as was the case in his study of allergies, only now during the second half of the twentieth century fully studied and explored. But as always his fame as a researcher, clinician, teacher and healer added extremely little to his own personal gain.

It sometimes happened that a wealthy family summoned him to their sick child and paid him well for his expert advice. On one occasion a member of the fabulous Rothschild banking family sought his help. For one such remuneration he could live quite adequately for a month devoted to scientific pursuits. But people of wealth were rare in a world of upheaval, and even so he was not always able to accept work as consultant physician, since the clinic and his research work had to come first. Though he was desperately in need of money, nothing would divert him from his investigations.

At last in 1918, Béla Schick was nominated Extraordinary Professor of Children's Diseases at the University of Vienna.

The title "extraordinary" is of particular interest. Austria was rapidly reaching a climax of reform. Out of desperation was to emerge a revolutionary spirit. But as yet many old concepts remained unchanged. One of these was that a man of Jewish parentage like Béla, was, no matter how able or how devoted to science and education, never actually attained the title of full professor of a university. The fact that he would perform the same academic tasks as others, and sometimes performed them more conscientiously and more effectively, made no difference to the authorities in the "Christian monarchy."

Béla, himself possessed of vast tolerance and always allowing for the weaknesses of mankind, would enjoy the telling of a story which made the rounds of Austria at this time. A well-known Viennese writer on educational and medical subjects was asked why he had never studied medicine formally. "Well," he replied without hesitation, "I didn't study before I reached the age of twenty because I was too young, and I didn't study between thirty and forty because I was too old."

There was a pause before the confused interrogator followed up with another question.

"Then why didn't you study between twenty and thirty?"

"Because I was a Jew," said the writer.

CHAPTER SEVENTEEN

An Incident with Flowers

THE WAR DREW TO AN EXHAUSTED CLOSE. BUT THAT WINTER OF 1918-19 was no period of relaxation or rejoicing for those in the position of Clemens von Pirquet and Béla Schick, confronted with the masses of children suffering hunger and illness in the aftermath of war. Yet whereas before there had been only misery, now there was hope. The relief organizations from the United States began supplying milk and other foods, medical necessities and clothing.

Neither Clemens and Béla, though tired almost beyond measure, could resist throwing themselves with enthusiasm into this new activity. Their clinical work, their experiments and studies must continue, but at the same time these new supplies must be used to the best advantage. The headquarters of the American Relief needed their experience and their medical skill, and so for the sake of the children these two doctors gave of their time and their genius to this new appeal.

From the first they introduced their scientifically proven system of nutrition, N.E.M., thus saving thousands of children from death by starvation.

Yet there is a limit to man's endurance. Both Béla and Clemens snatched only a few hours of sleep a night. With the approach of the summer of 1919 both were showing signs of exhaustion, and Clemens began to talk of vacation as an urgent necessity. He found it hard to get Béla to agree. But as it happened another call took Béla away from Vienna for a time.

His father Jacques had already passed his seventieth birthday, and urgent letters from Janka told Béla that father was rapidly failing in health. It was hardly surprising. The grain-buying firm of Jacques Schick in Graz had become bankrupt in 1908, despite the sincere efforts of his elder son Richard who was his business partner. All Jacques' tremendous energy, his vast capacity for work, had netted him no security for his advanced years. Now, unable to continue as his own master, he was forced to find work from others more successful than himself. The one favorable aspect was the fact that he had so many friends in his line of business.

Almost at once he found himself with a good position in Zalaegerszeg. This Hungarian town of ten thousand inhabitants was about fifty miles southeast of Graz. It had acquired some fame as a grain-buying center for Hungarian farmers. There the Schick family was obliged to live, on 6 Varkör Street, sadly leaving their beloved Graz.

The new life was hard for Jacques, unaccustomed as he had become to working a set schedule of hours, unable to break away from work when he felt fatigued. Something of the easy flow of living had been taken away from him. His spirit flagged, and with this came the realization that he was growing old. Both his sons, Richard and Béla, had helped all they could with hard-earned money, but Jacques' pride had not left him, and there was little they could do.

Janka knew what he needed. She knew that nothing would mend his spirits more than to have Béla home for a spell, and she was right. Jacques seemed to become his own self again. He expanded with pride at having Béla there—"our professor," as Jacques delighted in calling his son. His attitude toward his own work seemed to change. It was like a miracle for Janka to hear him telling Béla what fascinating work he was doing, to hear him describing all the colorful people that he encountered every day, from Hungarian laborers and farmers in their bright costumes to the wealthy buyers from Vienna and Budapest.

But there was no lack of interest on his part or on Janka's

in all the things Béla had done. He was pressed into telling everything in detail from his scientific work and his management of the clinic to his part in the nourishment of starved children and his contacts with the Americans in charge of the relief mission.

One evening his mother took Béla by surprise with a question to her husband, which he knew was intended for his ears as well.

"I wonder, Jacques," she said, "if they know in America of our son?"

Béla was embarrassed when his father smiled eagerly and nodded at him.

"They? In America?" Béla protested. "I'm not an opera singer, after all. If you mean the specialists in America, pediatricians, perhaps they know a little. Sometimes they write about my experiments. Sometimes they discuss various problems confronting doctors of children's diseases and they touch upon my name. But those are only specialists. For the people of America —even in America where there is lots of publicity for everything—there is not much they know about an ordinary scientific worker not even living there."

But Jacques would have none of this kind of modesty, and he cried out emphatically, "Full of possibilities—America! Oh, it must be a fascinating country. Béla, I think you should travel to America."

Janka looked anxious, and interrupted him. "Oh no, no! It's much too far. If he went there and lived there, how would we ever see him?"

"You spoke of it," said Jacques.

"I only mentioned America because of what our neighbor said. She told me yesterday that she has a brother in New York. He is a professor, or something of the sort. He deals with troubles of the brain, she said. But what kind of American professor could that be, with only four years of Gymnasium in Europe?"

"Well, he could have studied there," replied Jacques impatiently. "They certainly have universities in New York and learned people too. Not just cowboys and Indians."

Béla got up suddenly. It was an important moment for him.

"There must be something to this mental telepathy business, for as a matter of fact I have been thinking a good deal about visiting the United States some time."

He heard his mother's quick intake of breath. "No!"

But Jacques made an impatient gesture of the hand. "Give him a chance to speak, Janka."

"Clemens von Pirquet, he knows America quite well. He lectured there for some time. And—well, he told me they had even asked him about me. I could very easily, so Clemens says, get an invitation to lecture at some American university. Conditions are very different there. Everybody lives comfortably. And cultural life is growing. Education is growing too, becoming more and more advanced and modern. They need capable people in all branches. You can't imagine what tremendous possibilities there are in America for medicine—studies, lectures, experimentation, everything."

Béla was drawn out of his rhapsody by his mother's pathetic voice. "But it's so far away, so far . . . far from Graz, from Zalaegerszeg!"

"Oh, but I'm not going yet, Mother," he said quickly. "And who knows? I may never go."

"But you are thinking about it, and with you it is always the same, for if you begin to think about a thing, you end up by doing it, and quickly too."

"But look at Austria, look at Hungary, any of these countries. What's left of them? Vienna right now is overcrowded with professors and scholars and experts. And what can they do? They haven't a chance if they stay. Everybody's frightened here. Economically, we're bankrupt. Politically we are lost. But then again I could say that it is merely temporary. I think perhaps it is, and things will grow better, after a period." Béla was pacing the floor, and he seemed to be arguing with himself, more than speaking with the others.

"Oh, it will be better," his mother said quickly. "Things will get better with each dawning of a new day." She wanted it to be so enough to believe it would be so.

"If only you are right," sighed Jacques, and he looked tired again.

"It's hard to experiment here," mused Béla. "There is such a scarcity of equipment for one thing. But in America they have everything. Their laboratories. . . ."

"Then you are going?" Janka questioned. "Already going?"

"No, Mother, I've got things to do first. I have to learn how to play poker, how to play bridge, how to dance. All these are most important. And how to dodge newspaper reporters, for they can destroy anyone by the wrong publicity if they take a dislike to you, and with my English the way it is I might not say the right things."

"Where did you learn all this?" asked his father.

Béla smiled quickly. "Clemens told me." Béla had meant it as a sort of joke, but now he saw his parents were taking everything he said with great seriousness. He had to admit to himself there was a certain amount of prophetic truth in his words.

Janka suddenly laughed. "If I know you as well as I think I do, it's going to take you so long to become perfect in all these things you say are necessary—and perfect you'll have to be in every one before you'll be satisfied—that it'll be a long time before you'll be able to go. I know."

Béla sat down again, more at ease. "That's it, Mother. So you see, there's no worry. Play cards well, and dance, and be accepted in society, first. Then, and only then, success as a scientific scholar."

"A strange country!" Jacques shook his head, then added brightly. "But full of possibilities."

It was in this half bantering manner that America, the mythical country, was discussed.

By the 14th of August, Béla was back in Vienna, back at work at the Kinderklinik. In honor of his arrival he received a bouquet, ten budding roses, from the mother of one of his young patients. He handed the not yet fully open flowers to a maid at the clinic, asking her to put them in a vase and in his room. She did so promptly, with curious results.

In Béla's own words, this is what happened:

> I was extremely astonished on the next day, in the morning, when I noticed that the flowers had wilted.

I couldn't explain it to myself and when the serving girl arrived I questioned her, and she confessed to me that she was menstruating at the time and that all the flowers she touched during her period of menses withered at her touch.

I made many careful and detailed studies with many women and with many flowers, and always with the same result. The flowers wilted. It developed that people from the earliest times knew a great deal of this occurrence. But it had come to be considered another of the old wives' tales. A menstruating woman used not to be allowed into the garden, or into the fields or the orchards. They weren't even allowed to make marmalade. In history I found many examples of this.

By study I proved that a great number of women do not have a harmful flow, or only in a very small degree. I made countless other experiments during the course of several months, mostly with flowers and with yeast. I discovered that dough rises a smaller amount than normal when the woman handling the dough is menstruating. I made many other experiments with the menstrual blood and was able to show that a poison circulates in that blood. To all appearances it is in some respects connected to the red blood corpuscles. With the blood it travels to all sections of the body organism and is emitted from the body with the perspiration. Menstrual blood is entirely different from ordinary blood. It will not coagulate, and it will not easily wash out of clothing. I named this poisonous substance *menotoxine*. I have intentions of making further experiments—for example, the relation of menotoxine to the process of conception. I consider it an obligation of ours to be deeply indebted to people—to plain folks, for preserving this valuable information. Very often knowledge of this sort is recognized too late by intelligent scholars.

Béla wrote of this menstrual poison, menotoxine, in the year 1920 in the *Wiener Klinischen Wochenschrift*, number 19, under the title "Das Menstruationsgift." This work, conceived through an accident with ten roses, was the basis for many years' study by other workers.

CHAPTER EIGHTEEN

The Making of an Emigrant

THE FORTY-FIVE-YEAR-OLD PROFESSOR OF CHILDREN'S DISEASES AT the University of Vienna was so immersed in work that he hardly realized that his fame as an investigator was spreading out beyond Vienna, beyond Europe. Reports of his pioneer work and scientific experiments were included in the medical journals of Japan, China, the Soviet Union, Spain, Australia and the United States. Wherever medical institutions existed, wherever people noted the development of education and science, the name of Béla Schick was known.

Yet Béla was too busy to bother about what others thought of him. He was taken by surprise in the summer of 1922 when a letter came to him from George Blumenthal, the president of the Mount Sinai Hospital of New York. Would Béla be interested in assuming the directorship of the Pediatric Department of this outstanding medical institution? Béla was impressed, wondered why they should think of him for such an important post.

Mr. Blumenthal, on vacation in France, asked for an opportunity to meet the learned doctor somewhere in Europe to talk over the business. They met in Lucerne, Switzerland, in July of the same year. Mr. Blumenthal brought along his friend, Leo Arnstein, vice-president of Mount Sinai, in case he needed reserves in his effort to persuade Dr. Schick to come to America.

As it turned out, many factors operated in their favor. To begin with, the matter of remuneration was one which Béla ignored. He was so used to living on the barest essentials that he seemed scarcely aware of the value of American dollars. What Béla wanted to know was everything about conditions at the hospital for scientific experimentation. He was amazed at what he heard. If he accepted the position he would lack nothing. The war had left America unscathed. America was new and flourishing and productive. It needed men like Dr. Béla Schick.

What resistance remained in Béla after that was dissipated by the fact that his dearest friend, Clemens von Pirquet, who had for so long encouraged him to go to America, was himself preparing for another visit to the New World.

It was arranged that Béla would visit the United States in the following January, and would look around. He would get an impression of the great metropolis where perhaps he might spend the rest of his life, and he would see what the working conditions were for an earnest scholar and scientist. He returned to Vienna, to the Universitäts-Kinderklinik, and prepared himself for the momentous journey to the other side of the world.

A letter came from Graz. His parents had just moved back there, but Jacques was allowed no pleasant old age in retirement. In the seventy-fourth year of his life, while still a hard-working man, on August 2nd, he died of pneumonia. His funeral was attended by half the town of Graz, for Jacques was known and admired by most people as that rare type of human, industrious, friendly and charitable to all.

Béla hurried back to his mother. His trip to America would have to be canceled for Janka was in need of help. It was up to Béla and Richard now. But the situation was difficult. Though he did nothing further by way of preparation for his voyage, the news of his expected appearance in New York was spreading. Letters arrived practically every week with various propositions such as lectures at the universities, and addresses and readings at the medical societies of the larger cities. Harvard University nominated him as the 1923 Cutter Lecturer on Preventive Medicine, and his former American students from Vienna, themselves now assuming important roles at many of the universities in the United States, were pouring on him other propositions of a practical nature.

At first Béla tried to minimize these offers so that his mother would not worry about his going away. But Janka was not to be put off. She insisted on hearing about everything. Béla began to realize that his mother was no longer opposed to his leaving for America. Soon she detected Béla's hesitation, and she proceeded to argue him into going. She was over sixty years of age. But she did not look more than fifty and felt a good deal younger. Why should he ruin his own career by fearing for her? She was well able to look after herself.

Béla called a conference with his brother and sisters. Janka was to know nothing about it. At this conference the four agreed solemnly that each was to do what he or she could to see that Janka would never know poverty or worry again, and Béla in the presence of his brother and sisters pledged himself to send a set sum of money regularly from the United States.

So at last, after many waverings, in January, 1923, Professor Béla Schick came to New York. He was treated with great hospitality and he felt pleased, for New York was unlike any center he had known. He liked the fresh, new look of the city, which so well symbolized the mental climate. Here, he thought, was a dynamic and youthful community, made up of countless nationalities and all creeds, all bent on pushing on to success, exuding genuine optimism. He liked the American logic of numbering the streets and avenues. He liked the charm and grace of New Yorkers. Everybody was courteous and helpful.

Dr. S. S. Goldwater, the director of Mount Sinai Hospital, and other doctors of the rapidly expanding institution at Fifth Avenue and 100th Street, showed him around the hospital, emphasizing the excellent conditions for work should he become director of the Pediatric Department.

Two young doctors in particular, both former students of his, Dr. Abraham Zingher and Dr. Jerome S. Leopold, went to no end of trouble in assisting Béla with his plans.

On February 8th, Béla delivered his first Cutter Lecture at the Harvard Medical School on "Prevention and Control of Diphtheria." For this he received the sum of fifty dollars. When he returned, he found that a reception had been arranged for him at the home of Dr. Zingher. He encountered a group of noted doctors and educators—and a number of most eligible young ladies. Among the latter was Margaret E. Fries, a serious-minded person and a pediatrician in her own right. Béla found her most attractive and a stimulating conversationalist, though at the time he had no idea how momentous this meeting was to prove for him.

After a few weeks Béla felt he had familiarized himself with conditions at the hospital; he returned to Europe at the close of February to wind up his affairs in the Old World and become an emigrant to the New.

It was not difficult for Béla to obtain his visa. To the Commissioner of Immigration of the U.S. Department of Labor, Henry S. Curran; to Augustus S. Downing of the New York State Department of Education; and to the Commissioner of Health, Dr. Matthias Nicoll, Jr., of the State of New York Department of Health in Albany were sent letters of esteem, admiration and endorsement by such persons as Dr. Walter L. Niles, Dean of the Medical School of Cornell University; Dr. William J. Mayo of Mayo Clinic fame; Dr. Simon Flexner of the Rockefeller Institute for Medical Research; U.S. Senator Royal S. Copeland; Dr. Herbert B. Wilcox, Professor at Columbia University College of Physicians and Surgeons; and Dr. John Howland, Pediatrician in Chief of the Johns Hopkins Hospital.

The modest Viennese professor, so gracious, genial, sincere and profound in knowledge, had made friends with everyone he met in New York. They had all liked him from the first meeting, and now they were all anxious to expedite his return.

In a letter to the New York State Department of Education, Dr. William H. Park, a prominent bacteriologist and chief of the Bureau of Laboratories of the Department of Health of New York City, expressed the general feeling:

> Owing to the fact of my interest in diphtheria, I have been closely in touch with Dr. Schick in his researches in immunology and especially because of his development of the Schick test for the detection

of immunity to diphtheria. American medicine has been
stimulated by many Americans coming under the influence of Dr. Schick in his hospital in Vienna. There
is no question that he is among the foremost men in
pediatrics and in certain lines of immunology and also
that he has contributed greatly to the progress of medicine by teaching those who have come in contact
with him.

Dr. Park had touched on one highly important point—the role
of Béla Schick in the expansion of medical knowledge in the
United States. His role was not restricted to immunology, but
included many other branches of medicine.

Despite all the efforts of his new friends in America, Béla
did not find it at all easy to pack his things and leave his
native land. He felt utterly disorganized. It seemed to him he
would never be ready to leave on the appointed day, and at
times he debated with himself whether the whole project was
worth all the trouble. This whole period seemed to him like a
ghastly waste of time during which he should be working. As
it happened his old friend von Pirquet decided the issue for him.

Clemens accepted an offer to work for a time at the University of Minnesota's Department of Pediatrics. He would make
the voyage over with Béla Schick. Béla was delighted. Now he
had no more doubts about his departure.

On August 16th he received a letter from a former student,
Woodward Colby, was now a doctor at the Miller Hospital Clinic
in St. Paul, Minnesota. It shows what fast friends Béla made
of his students, and what a deep impression he made upon them.
Young Colby wrote:

> There has been a new pediatrician added to the
> ranks, one who strongly recommends your feeding method
> because he owes his enviable weight curve to a start
> with seventeen per cent sugar. From five and one half
> pounds he jumped to eight and one half in six weeks.
> He surely is a dandy baby, and we are very happy
> with him.
>
> Since leaving Wien we have been very busy. My

connection with the Miller Clinic has given me plenty of material from the start. In the newborn ward, I have cared for about 300 cases with a high percentage of excellent weight curves...

Colby did not know that Béla was coming to the United States, but he wrote of Clemens' expected visit in this way:

We are excited and immensely pleased over the Pirquets coming to our university. Our hope is that the opportunities for work in his field will be great enough to keep Professor Pirquet with us. At present, the scope of the work is not as broad as in Vienna, but with a splendid endowment which has recently been made for a new children's hospital, Dr. Pirquet will doubtless have, within a few years, a hospital and clinic at Minnesota as famous as yours in Vienna.

We like to think of you as head of the Kinderklinik. Your first duty must be to convince little Dr. Wagner to limit his cigarettes to three a day and then to get married. Although I talked to him long and earnestly on both subjects it was of no avail. Perhaps you won't find it so futile. But seriously, please give Dr. Wagner, Dr. Kassowitz and Dr. Nobel my best regards and to you, dear Dr. Schick, we send our very best wishes.

Béla's anxiety over the voyage he was about to make was fully comprehended by Dr. Goldwater, director of Mount Sinai Hospital. He understood it was Béla's nature to be scrupulous and correct in everything, and he wanted to be sure that all would run smoothly, that he would not have to get into any unhappy arguments with immigration officers. Yes, Dr. Goldwater understood without difficulty and wrote to Béla on September 4th:

I am in receipt of your letter of August 8th, announcing your sailing date and the name of your steamer, and as I am uncertain whether this reply will reach you in Vienna, I am writing it in duplicate and sending

one copy to Hamburg in care of your steamer, and
the other to your Vienna address.

I enclose herewith a brief note which is sent in
response to your request for an 'official letter' regarding
the object of your sailing. Regular meetings of the Board
of Trustees are not held during the summer and it
is impossible at this time to obtain a formal resolution
of the board. I suppose, however, what you really want
is some written indication from the hospital of the position which awaits you here, to exhibit in case of need,
to government authorities in Europe, and if this is so,
perhaps the enclosed note, which I have signed as director
of the hospital, will suffice. . . .

I anticipate no trouble on your arrival here, in view
of the very clear and cordial letter which Mr. Arnstein
obtained in July, from the local Commissioner of Immigration. I believe that a copy of this letter has already
been sent to you, but in order to make sure of the
matter I am enclosing another copy. This may be shown
to the immigration agents in New York, if any question
is raised by them; but if and when that happens, the
undersigned or some representative of the board will
be present to take part in the proceedings and to smooth
out any difficulty that may develop. . . .

And in answer to Béla's request for material concerning the
background of Mount Sinai Hospital, Dr. Goldwater wrote:

I regret my inability to send you 'a book containing
the history and organization of Mount Sinai, especially
the history of the children's department.' A comprehensive history of the hospital has never been written, nor is
any special record of the past of the children's department available. Unless we are very much mistaken, the
real history of the children's department lies in the
future—you will see from this that the hospital has the
utmost confidence in its future pediatrician.

My best wishes for a pleasant journey. You may
count confidently upon anything that I can do personally
or officially to assist you in adapting yourself to the

unaccustomed conditions of life and work which you are
about to face in New York.

It is worth noting that not until 1952 did a book on Mount
Sinai appear, entitled *The First Hundred Years of The Mount
Sinai Hospital*, written by Joseph Hirsh and Beka Doherty.

With the aid of capable and obliging people, who helped
him disentangle the "red tape" of rules and regulations associated with the voyage to the United States, which so discom-
forted the professor from Vienna, the chapters dealing with his
European work and life draw to a close.

On September 30, 1923, Béla Schick landed on American soil
to take up permanent residence, and to devote himself to enriching medical knowledge and practice in the United States.

CHAPTER NINETEEN

Cathy

IT WAS CHARACTERISTIC OF BÉLA THAT ONLY TWO DAYS AFTER HIS arrival, before he had even found an apartment to live in, he was hard at work at Mount Sinai Hospital. There were sick children. They must be taken care of. Béla regarded that as a sacred obligation.

Nevertheless he needed an apartment where he could find rest and quiet when he needed them. There was the possibility, too, that he could conduct a limited private practice. Dr. Jerome S. Leopold came to the rescue. He had a cousin who knew of a place, and Béla rented it immediately. It was a modest four-room apartment on the ground floor of 17 East 84th Street. Béla went to the large department stores, Wanamaker's and Macy's, to buy his furniture and everything else necessary to fit up an attractive bachelor residence and doctor's office.

For the first few weeks Béla devoted every free moment to writing letters back home. He wrote to each member of his family, to all of the many friends who had helped him on his journey, then to the countless friends in Vienna. Béla had always thought more of maintaining friendships, of establishing harmony and good feeling, than of using those around him to further any personal ambition.

In New York he had already made many friends, but at the same time he began to sense the advanced tempo of this modern city. No man was more devoted to work than Béla Schick, and he appreciated great earnestness in others, but he felt estranged from those who had their sights fixed too firmly on some preconceived goal of success. This, he felt, inevitably resulted in a certain callousness and insincerity.

Now, writing to so many close friends so far away, Béla began to feel a touch of sadness at finding himself in a new land with only new faces around him. Would he like America? He still did not know. Sometimes now Béla would experience a deeply romantic mood. He would dream of finding in this teeming city the real and perfect love, someone who would want to share his life with him, someone he could confide in and be happy with.

It was on such an occasions, when Béla was feeling a certain warmth and pleasure within him, a certain undefinable confidence over a future happiness, that he came again upon Margaret Fries, the friend of Dr. Zingher he had met on his first visit. Béla was attracted by her elegant apearance. She knew how to dress well, to set off her natural good looks. Béla saw this as a practical side of her over-all efficiency. For Dr. Margaret E. Fries was efficient. She had been educated as a doctor, at a time when women doctors were something of a rarity. She took pride in the fact, and showed by her efficiency and her strength of character that she was not to be regarded as anything less for being a woman. Some doctors thought she carried the matter to unnecessary lengths, and some of them made references to a rather domineering attitude.

Béla was not convinced. He liked her scientific mind from the first. He admired her courage and her sincerity. There was no lack of subjects for conversation with Margaret, for she liked nothing better than to talk of medicine. Did she want more than friendship from him? Béla wondered one day as he accepted an invitation from Margaret to visit her parents' home.

Her father, Albert Fries, was connected with a real estate company. He was well enough off to live more than comfortably, and to give his two daughters an excellent education. Both were university graduates, not too usual an occurrence for women at the beginning of the twentieth century. It was Albert Fries' idea that both his girls should grow up to be independent. Thus Margaret went into the medical profession, and his older daughter Catharine Carrie took up the study of law.

It was in visiting the Fries household upon Margaret's invitation that Béla met Catharine Carrie, known affectionately by her friends as Cathy. Though she was sixteen years younger than Béla, she had already studied at Columbia University and New York University, where she had obtained the degree of Doctor of Jurisprudence, and she now worked with Strook & Strook, a law firm, where she stayed about two years. Cathy was not like her younger sister. She had no wish to sacrifice for her career. The pleasures of life were too enchanting. She would become rhapsodic over concerts. She was an ardent theater-goer. She was always planning trips to new places, meeting new people. She enjoyed everybody, and in turn her vivacious charm attracted others. Béla was no exception.

Cathy was on the tall side, about five feet seven, with a nicely proportioned figure. She had dark brown hair, neatly trimmed and short. Her eyes were brown and sparkling with the pleasure of living. Fortune favored her. Her parents indulged her. Her smile seemed to gain her all she desired. Yet she was not spoiled. Béla watched with amazement, then was flattered to find that she was paying an unusual amount of attention to him.

During the fall of 1923, buttons the size of a nickel were introduced with a dark blue background and white lettering which read: "I AM SCHICKED! ARE YOU?" The first of these buttons was given to Béla himself by the Schick staff of the Boston Health Department. Cathy got hold of one somewhere and pinned it to her blouse, as if to scandalize and bewilder her mother and sister. The fact was that both Béla and Cathy had fallen in love. And with the exception of the innocent flirtations of Cathy during the past few years and Béla's brief infatuation for a certain Russian woman, who had two children, this love of theirs was a new and exciting experience for both.

Everyone who surmised the situation wished them success, for they knew that this would be a well-matched happy couple. Cathy had no desire, as have many other women, to reform her future husband, nor to force her own will on him. She showed only how anxious she was to help him in all his undertakings. She never wished to impress him with her own intelligence and learning. A professional career, with that certain independence which went with it, never meant to her what it did to her younger sister.

There existed among some of Béla's friends a question as to which of the two daughters of Albert Fries Béla was most interested in. Among those in doubt were three women doctors at Mount Sinai Hospital, who worked under Béla and formed what they chose to call "Schick's harem." There was the American Anne Topper, working with him on the problem of metabolism in pediatrics; the Hungarian Mitzi Freund, working on hematology; and the Viennese Rose Spiegel, working on allergy.

They knew how to get a smile from Béla by singing the song Anne Topper had written him, which went something like this:

> Three little maids from Sinai we
> Hanging around to learn you see
> Symptom, signs and therapeeee.
>
> This little maid from Vienna of late,
> I from Hungary to find a mate,
> I'm Miss America, I hope I rate.
>
> Three little maidens for your harem
> Await your words if you can spare 'em.
> Please, oh please, don't try to scare 'em,
> But be their Shiek if you can bear 'em.
> Three little maids are we.

But the three little maids who were very fond of Béla had noticed for some time the change that had come over him. He was still very busy, but not with such an air of preoccupation as before. There were times when he would engage them in conversation about matters outside the hospital. His discussion would drift over to the question of the likes and dislikes of young ladies generally, on favorite hats and favorite dresses and favorite colors. The "harem" perceived that each week their chief was making swift progress in his latest venture, and they wondered: Was it Margaret or was it Cathy?

Even the children became aware of a change in their doctor's mood. He spent more time with them, playing as if he were a child himself. He demonstrated with his hands how shadow animals could be made to appear on the hospital wall. He built houses out of their blocks. He sang with them, and played tunes on their musical toys. One of his "harem" even caught him fascinating a group of open-mouthed convalescents by performing real magic tricks. Of course it was well known throughout the world that Dr. Schick knew how to play with children. It was Béla's argument that play is one of the most important moments in the therapy of the child.

Nevertheless, during this period at Mount Sinai Hospital Béla broke all records with his play activity. It aroused some criticism from his primer colleagues, who felt that he played with the children in the wards too much and too long, and that he showed little regard for the prestige and standards of his high position. But nothing could change Béla for, if he happened to hear of this form of criticism, he would whistle quietly to himself, and then go on behaving just as before.

Petty criticism could have little effect upon a man as eminently successful as Béla Schick. His writings were no longer read by merely a select few. American doctors all over the country had come to realize the importance of his discoveries. Béla found himself sought after as never before. So many in his profession wanted to hear him lecture, to speak with him, to know him. They welcomed his quick friendliness, his lack of pretense, his desire to give more than receive. He put strangers at ease. He even made them laugh, sometimes without intending to, which made him laugh more than ever.

Béla was never a powerful speaker, and his lectures towards the beginning of his stay in the United States were full of odd book-learned English phrases. For those who had studied in Vienna, his words were full of significance, but for those limited to the American-English tongue they were, to say the least, hard sledding. Then again he would interlard his speeches with curious expressions of his own such as his "percentage from hundred."

Percentage is calculated from a hundred, everyone knew, but Béla was concerned with the idea that accurate conclusions must be taken from at least one hundred cases. Perhaps in a certain town injections are made, and a certain number of children become sick from some unknown illness. To say 50 per cent might mean only twenty children. "If we are to make any accounting in medical statistics," Béla explained, "we must have at least a minimum of one hundred cases. And from these hundred we draw our scientific data."

Béla continued: "On the other hand, too many experimental examples may present inaccuracies in experience. Just as too few are not enough on which to build accurate statistics. One hundred cases must be obtained, correct, in order to have an accurate picture, or as was mentioned percentage from hundred."

After one of these lectures in Manhattan, Béla received an ovation. Later, when he had left the hall with the Fries sisters and their father, Cathy remarked: "I guess we four were the only people who understood the lecture."

Béla looked puzzled, "Then why were they applauding so loud?"

Mr. Fries exclaimed with an easy smile as he placed an arm around the doctor's shoulder, "Why, out of kindness and respect for the lecturer."

But the famous lecturer quite rapidly became converted to the American-English idiom.

In the summer of 1925, before his departure for Europe on a vacation to visit his mother, a group of doctor colleagues arranged a farewell dinner in his honor. Two noted physicians, both adherents of the Schick medical theories, spoke: Dr. Abraham Zingher and Dr. William H. Park.

An interesting highlight of the evening was the dinner menu, which ran as follows:

MENU

canteloupe à la Klebs-Löffler
gumbo toxin in vials

radishes two plus minus
fillet sole de guinea pig
broiled breast of schick-en
combined with
new peas von Behringum
salad research laboratory
sauce de mosquito bites
ice cream diphtheritica
ginger snaps
demi-tox
cigars lethalis
platinum tipped cigarettes

When Béla returned to New York in September on the S.S. Republic, a formidable group from Mount Sinai, including his "harem," assembled to greet him at the pier. To everyone's astonishment Béla came walking down the gangplank hand in hand with Cathy. Béla's answer to the shouts of greeting came simultaneously with Cathy's: "We're engaged. We became engaged on board ship in the middle of the Atlantic."

It was finally divulged that Cathy had left without anyone's knowledge on the boat immediately after Béla's. They had met in Europe, and had spent the most enchanting vacation of their entire lives. Alone together, away from the prying eyes and gossiping tongues of their own circle of acquaintances, Béla and Cathy were able to discover how much they suited each other, until the loveliest prospect had become that of sharing the rest of their lives.

It was not so very long after that September surprise before their friends received the following communication by mail:

Mr. and Mrs. Albert Fries
announce the marriage of their daughter
Catharine Carrie
to
Dr. Béla Schick
on Thursday the third of December
One thousand nine hundred and twenty-five
Nine West Eighty-second Street
NEW YORK

CHAPTER TWENTY

From New York to the World

AMONG THOSE CHARGED WITH THE ADMINISTRATION OF MOUNT Sinai Hospital there was great enthusiasm over the methods of Dr. Schick. No man was more persevering and meticulous in all he set out to do. He literally and enthusiastically buried himself in his work. But certain observers did wish he would take a broader view of medical problems. Among these was his devoted friend Dr. Abraham Zingher, assistant director of the New York City Research Laboratories, who started a one-man campaign to influence Béla.

While Béla and von Pirquet were both excellent clinicians, they had a difference in viewpoint which made them find different methods with which to attack any major medical problem. Clemens, remaining in Austria, had advanced by a gradual and systematic process from clinician and teacher to the role of reformer, and reorganizer of the public health system in his own country. For Clemens was interested first in the sickness as such, then in its negative functions in the community.

But Béla's attitude was different. Instead of regarding a sick child as merely a small fraction of humanity, as his friend did, Béla saw in one child the whole of humanity. That particular child demanded all his attention. Out of the deep observation he gave to that one child would come his theories on therapy.

But Dr. Zingher saw a drawback to this point of view. While

Béla's experiments and his theories and practice were invaluable to the medical profession, he was doing nothing toward promoting understanding and enlightenment among the people as a whole. The mass of people, argued Zingher, needed to be educated too. The voice of such a close friend was a powerful influence on Béla, but it still took time for Dr. Zingher to convince Béla of the wisdom of a more active role in the community in the struggle against diphtheria and tuberculosis.

Béla's resistance lay in his desire to spend all his so-called free time in the laboratory. He argued that someone else should assume the role of acquainting the public with certain medical problems and popularizing them. But to the delight of Dr. Zingher and other persuasive friends, Béla began to weaken. Immediately the word got around, and Béla found himself swamped with obligations.

On January 6, 1927, he was accepted as a   llow of the New York Academy of Medicine, where on October 29 of the same year he delivered a lecture to an overflowing audience on "Certain Aspects of Tuberculosis in Infancy." In the same year he was chosen by the New York Board of Health as a consulting physician to the Willard Parker Hospital, the hospital for contagious diseases. This was, naturally, without compensation.

At Sea View Hospital where Béla was director of the Pediatric Department an elaborate entertainment was presented on his fiftieth birthday by the children of the Sea View School. The children, before over 300 guests, presented Béla with a bouquet of flowers grown in their school garden. The employees contributed an immense birthday cake, while friends presented him with a portrait of himself.

The school's teachers had arranged an entertainment, a program of dances and songs, and a birthday poem written by the children.

Special tribute was paid to Béla during the program by the hospital medical board and the nurses.

That same year, Béla had an appendectomy performed on him at Mount Sinai. He had diagnosed the ailment himself and ordered the operation performed with a local anesthetic so that he could observe, with the aid of a mirror, how the inside of his abdomen looked and how the operation was progressing. Though the diagnosis was wrong since the appendix proved to be healthy, Béla remarked to the doctors surrounding his bedside as he lapsed off into restful sleep: "This operation is a removal of trouble that might have developed in the future."

In the meantime a campaign of persuasion had started against him. This was a woman's campaign, and it came from Cathy. Though herself happily married, and well adjusted, she was convinced that her husband was working himself too hard.

This was a new experience for Béla. All his life he had worked steadily and concentratedly, conscious only of the scant time given man to accomplish even half his plans. Living as a bachelor there had seemed little purpose in relaxation.

With Cathy it was different. She knew well enough how to appeal to him. She could always recall their beautiful experience together when traveling through Europe before their marriage. She could always emphasize his love of the arts. They had that in common—concerts, theater, art exhibits. They both loved to see new places and faces, and all the hustle and bustle of travel delighted them. Nevertheless, Cathy was too clever to base all her arguments upon such considerations, for she knew Béla could always put aside all personal pleasures for the sake of his work. No. Béla, she proposed triumphantly, should combine his work with pleasure. What Dr. Zingher said was right. For the cause of medicine, Béla should go out and campaign, spread his ideas by word of mouth, not only in New York, not only in America, but even abroad. And wherever he went she would go with him. They would travel in leisure, accomplishing some important part of his work while living for enjoyment as human beings should.

The argument convinced Béla. It fell in with his own conclusions, now that he had become persuaded by his friends. So every summer, if he did not make a voyage to Europe with Cathy for some pediatricians' congress, or for a meeting on tuberculosis, or for some international debate or discussion on allergies, or to deliver some scientific lecture in Paris, Oslo, Moscow, London or Zurich, then he traveled through the United States, Mexico or Canada.

All his trips, whether in Europe or America, were made in the company of his devoted Cathy, and usually with several doctor acquaintances who "were traveling in that direction," and all these trips were tied in with some university, hospital or some international medical institute; yet Cathy saw to it that Béla relaxed and set aside the problems of medicine as much as possible.

Béla's greatest curiosity concerning people was what they did with their hands to express their delight in living; he and Cathy brought home trunkfuls of such products: Mexican hand-made ceramics, Salzburg toys, French antiques, and so on. Neither Béla nor Cathy knew the actual value of these things. They were often aware of the fact that they were being taken in by some wild story, or actually cheated. Still they bought what they liked, and that was the only thing that concerned them. They had definite proof that they had been swindled. There were those ancient knives, supposed to have been used during the founding of the Scythian State, sold to them in Vienna. They found out afterwards that the knives had actually been made in Iran about thirty or forty years ago. They laughed about that a good deal. Then there was the copper watering can supposedly made under the aegis of *Le Roi Soleil*, Louis XIV. . . . They always had fun over their own innocence.

But their greatest joy lay in collecting children's toys, toys they picked up from all over the world; some new, some old, some valuable, some worthless, but always amusing. With these they packed their New York home, and distributed hundreds more among Béla's small patients.

The demand for Béla's services was overwhelming, not only from private individuals, but also from medical institutions in New York and throughout the country. Béla could have made an enormous amount of money. But he never did, because he never tried to. Having lived in near-poverty for most of his youth he was now satisfied if he made a comfortable living, if he earned enough to travel without worry, but without affluence. Béla had peculiar set patterns of behavior. Some called him miserly, others a do-gooder.

The first accusation derived from his way of handling traveling expenses. Regardless of who traveled with them, Béla paid only for his wife and himself. When a group went to a restaurant, Béla would make sure that two checks were rendered, separately—one for himself and his wife, the other for those who dined with them. If they took a taxi, he would calculate exactly how much he owed so as to pay for his share and no more. He dealt with all minor expenses in this fashion, and if he noticed a bewildered expression on the face of a friend, he would remark: "If you are able to afford a trip, you should be able to afford the minor expenses as well." However irritating this statement might be, it was logical.

But on the other hand these same critics could not understand why, in a case where Béla should have charged five hundred dollars for a consultation, he charged only fifty dollars. Often he would travel from Manhattan to some sick child in Brooklyn or the Bronx or farther, and waste half a day, returning to his office without a penny.

If he was questioned, Béla replied: "My conscience won't allow me to accept money from poor people." That was how it had been in Vienna, and that was how it remained in New York. Naturally, some of his private consultations brought him several hundred dollars a week, but even for these he never established the fee himself, for he never wanted to become involved in money matters. When he was asked: "How much?" he would answer: "Whatever you're able to afford."

For Béla, medicine was his life; in spreading knowledge for the benefit of the people he gave freely of himself and his time and expected no compensation. The campaign against diphtheria is a superb example.

One of the earliest eyewitness accounts of diphtheria in North America was Dr. William Douglass' short publication entitled "The Practical History of New Epidemical Eruptive Miliary Fever with an Angina Ulcusculosa, Which Prevailed in Boston, New England in the Years 1735 and 1736." There were new epidemic outbreaks during the years of 1752 to 1755 in New York, and again in 1770. By this time the various forms of diphtheria were known, namely, tonsillar, pharyngeal, tracheal and bronchial. The malignant form was also known, although it was frequently confused with other forms of septic sore throat. By the beginning of the twentieth century the disease had begun to come under some control in Europe. But in the United States the real war against diphtheria began in the twenties. At this time the Commissioner of Health of New York City was Dr. Shirley W. Wynne, who was remarkably well equipped to carry on such a campaign. The heart of the struggle was naturally Béla Schick, who served as head of the Technical Consultation Board of the Diphtheria Commission. All of the city's medical societies were represented on this board.

In addition, a so-called Diphtheria Prevention Commission was formed from among the more noted personages of New York society with Thomas W. Lamont as its head. Among its members were Jeremiah Milbank, Cornelius N. Bliss, Nicholas Murray Butler, George F. Canfield, Robert W. De Forest, Lee K. Frankel, Walter E. Frew, Michael Friedsam, Mrs. Charles Dana Gibson, Rabbi Herbert S. Goldstein, Edwin Gould, Charles Hayden, Cardinal Hayes, Frederic A. Juilliard, John A. Kingsbury, Darwin P. Kingsley, Walter Laidlaw, Lieut. Gov. Herbert H. Lehman, Clarence H. Mackay, Bishop William T. Manning, Louis Marshall, Charles G. Meyer, Roswell Miller, Mrs. Courtlandt Nicoll, William Church Osborn, James H. Post, Frederick B. Pratt, Roland L. Redmond, Mrs. Ogden Mills Reid, Charles H. Sabin, William Jay Schieffelin, Paul M. Warburg, Rabbi Stephen S. Wise, and Henry C. Wright.

Not only did Dr. Schick take charge of the technical aspects of the campaign, but he also delivered speeches on the radio and wrote articles for the press informing the public and particularly the parents.

On March 22, 1929, Béla delivered the following radio address:

> The United States diphtheria record for 1927 was in round numbers 100,000 cases, with about 10,000 registered deaths. This means that 10,000 people died in the United States during 1927 from a disease which could have been avoided. What an amount of suffering, what an amount of sorrow, could have been spared

the parents of these children had they known that this disease could have been avoided.

Two-thirds of all cases of diphtheria occur before the tenth year of life and more than 80 per cent of the deaths from diphtheria occur between the ages of one and five years. Our young children are, therefore, in danger of contracting this disease and of dying of it. And it is a treacherous disease. The first symptoms are so indefinite that the mother can easily overlook their presence. It is necessary, even for the physician, to look for signs of the disease in order to discover them, as the child does not necessarily complain of pain in the throat, and at the beginning of the disease there is often not more than one or two spots on the tonsil.

We know the germ which causes the disease, and we know that the germ, the diphtheria bacillus, produces a poison, called diphtheria toxin, which endangers the health and the life of the child.

In New York, where Dr. William H. Park and his collaborators started the campaign against diphtheria, the situation is still, despite their excellent efforts, far from satisfactory. There are still about 15,000 cases of diphtheria in New York yearly, with over 700 deaths. The Health Department has not the same power to fight diphtheria that it has to prevent smallpox. It is difficult for the health authorities to reach the homes. They do reach the schools, and through the teachers the school children. But it is of even more importance that parents of preschool-age children be reached. The success of the fight to eradicate diphtheria depends largely upon the cooperation of the general public, and especially of the mothers of small children.

Forty-eight special diphtheria prevention clinics are now being maintained by the Health Department, and since January 19, the date of their opening, about 12,000 children have been completely immunized against the disease in these clinics. Besides this, a large number of family physicians have immunized many children in their private practises. I think parents who know that it is now possible to prevent diphtheria, and who nevertheless fail to have their children immunized, take too great a responsibility upon their shoulders.

The campaign started in 1927, when Béla Schick, being childless himself, persuaded his friend Abraham Zingher to be among the first to have his children immunized. It became a strong argument for the campaign; both of the men used it in their efforts to break down parent resistance. The campaign was brought into the schools, where the children were given slips to be signed by their parents authorizing their immunization.

Many amusing stories were circulated at this time—amusing but none the less true. When the Board of Health of Harrison, New Jersey, sent letters to parents asking permission to give the Schick test to their children, one mother sent back an abrupt note: "I refuse positively to permit either of my boys to take the Schick test. I have read the book and seen the play, and I want you to know I don't approve of them." Clearly she was under the influence of some Arabian prince.

The anti-diphtheria campaign through the years 1927-32 in New York City was financed by the city, the Metropolitan Life Insurance Company and the Milbank Memorial Fund. Eighty-five million pieces of literature were distributed. The campaign was pressed forward by physicians, by the press, the radio, churches and other community organizations.

The Metropolitan Life Insurance Company and other organizations distributed many millions of "Train Tickets to No-Diphtheria Town," as well as pamphlets entitled: "To the Schick Test." Inside was the simple story of a boy, Fred, who died of diphtheria, and on the last page an appeal to the parents, "Save Your Child From Diphtheria." The message ran:

> Your child need not have diphtheria. Science has made it possible for you to give absolute protection to your child. Some children are protected by nature, and will never contract the disease. Other children are susceptible to it. By means of the Schick Test you can find out to which class your child belongs. The Schick Test consists in giving the child a tiny injection in the skin of the arm. If, after a few days, a red spot

appears where the injection was made, the child is liable to have diphtheria. Children who might contract diphtheria as shown by the Schick Test may be protected against it by the Toxin-Antitoxin treatment. This treatment consists of three injections of vaccine, one each week for three weeks. The test and the vaccine treatment are harmless and are saving the lives of hundred of children.

Every child should be Schick tested.

You owe it to your child.

The role of Dr. Schick as a scientist at the head of the campaign to eliminate an infectious disease in the United States was important and far-reaching. He worked without rest, without remuneration in order to preserve the lives of America's children.

Diphtheria gradually came under control and has almost disappeared as a threat to human life, not only in New York but in all of the United States as well. As for Béla, one of his greatest treasures is an album he received in 1933 signed by a million grateful New York children as a memento of this successful campaign.

Five years later, Dr. G. Ramon of the Pasteur Institute, in a 25-page article on the control of diphtheria in the *Journal of The Mount Sinai Hospital,* emphasized the important role of Dr. Schick in the American campaign. The article began:

> Quelques années avant sa mort, Emile Roux qui, en 1887, avait découvert la toxine diphtérique, recevait à l'Institut Pasteur Béla Schick. 'Vous avez,' lui dit-il, 'fait accomplir un grand progrès à l'étude de l'immunité antidiphtérique. La réaction de Schick en fournissant un moyen très commode de mesurer le degré de cette immunité a rendu possible la démonstration rapide de l'efficacité de la vaccination contre la diphtérie. . . .

Towards the close of 1932 there appeared a book titled *Child Care Today,* by Béla Schick and William Rosenson. Into this book Béla poured all of his knowledge of prenatal care and of both the physical and mental growth and care of infants and children. It was a comprehensive book, but was written in simple, natural terms. This is "a great help to mothers and a valuable addition to our child care volumes," commented Dr. Haven Emerson. A few months after the book's publication, Béla received the gold medal of the Phi Lambda Kappa fraternity, national medical society, "for conspicuous achievement in the medical sciences." Then five months later, he was elected Honorary Member of the Society for Pediatric Research.

While up to his ears in the campaign against diphtheria, Béla still found time to wage a war against another disease—for many generations the most destructive illness of mankind—which demanded proper diagnosis and long periods of therapy. This disease was tuberculosis.

Aided by a grant from the Metropolitan Life Insurance Company, a group of doctors, including William H. Park, Camille Kereszturi Cayley, Milton Levine, Peter Vogel, Charles Hendee Smith, Frederick Bartlett, and Béla Schick began experimental work in 1927 in the Sea View, Bellevue, Harlem, Fifth Avenue, Mount Sinai, Greenpoint and Staten Island hospitals. They experimented on the so-called BCG vaccination, the Bacillus Calmette Guérin method.

When Béla delivered a lecture at the Buffalo Academy of Medicine, the *Buffalo Evening News* of March 18, 1931 published an interview with him, explaining the method.

> 'It is a culture of the bovine tubercle bacillus made absolutely innocuous by a particular method of culture,' Dr. Schick explained. 'Originally, it was applied mostly to newborn babies during the first ten days of life and administered by mouth. Later on it was used for older children and adults, and given by hypodermic injection.
> 'Only those free of tuberculosis can be treated by this method.
> 'This study has been actively carried on in human beings for ten years. At first it was limited almost entirely to France and thus far approximately 300,000 children have been treated there. In the world

1,000,000 people have received the treatment. In New York 400 children have been vaccinated under the most careful research methods. The Health Commissioner of Nashville, Tennessee, has personally directed the vaccination of 5,000 school children.'

Dr. Kereszturi Cayley, who had participated in the interview, actively entered the discussion with this statement:

It is now definitely known that the Calmette method is harmless and does some good. The degree of immunity, good or resistance which it can achieve needs further study.

The year before this, Béla had represented the National Tuberculosis Association of the United States at the International Union against Tuberculosis at Oslo, Norway. Béla had become a recognized leading authority on the subject. Among his many studies in this field was the classic work *Common Forms of Childhood Tuberculosis.*

In this book, in his characteristic manner Béla praised the achievements of doctors Ghon and Winternitz, as well as von Pirquet's cutaneous test, Mantoux's intracutaneous test, and H. Vollmer's "patch test." He wrote:

We have substituted the Pirquet test with the 'patch test' developed by H. Vollmer in the children's department of Mount Sinai and Sea View hospitals. My experience with this patch test has been so satisfactory that I believe that it will become the test of choice for the practitioner. Filter paper is soaked with a potent concentrated old tuberculin and dried. The paper is then cut up in squares of 1-cm. size. Two such squares of filter paper are attached to a piece of adhesive plaster. In the middle between these squares is put a third square of plain filter paper or filter paper soaked in plain bouillon (without tuberculin), acting as a control. The skin of the sternal region is cleansed with ether or benzine and the adhesive plaster simply applied to the skin. The perspiration dissolves the tuberculin of the filter paper and thus the tuberculin is absorbed.

The plaster should remain 48 hours in contact with the skin. After that time the adhesive plaster should be removed. The reaction may be read on the same day, but it is preferable to watch the reaction another 48 hours. In case of a positive reaction an inflammatory redness and small papules or vesicles appear corresponding to the field of the filter paper wheras the control shows normal skin. Irritations caused by the adhesive plaster are rarely seen to be so intensive that the reading of the test is made difficult. The advantage of this patch test is self-evident. No needle or borer is necessary. The child is not frightened by the preparation and application of the test. There is no painful sticking or scratching. The opposition of the parents to testing can also be easily overcome. I believe that the patch test of Vollmer will facilitate the campaign against tuberculosis.

The positive tuberculin test proves the existence of a tuberculous focus in the body, but not necessarily an active process. In infants and children up to three and four years of age the positive test can be taken as a sign of a relatively active process, because the tuberculous infection needs at least two to four years before it is arrested. The older the child the less we can rely on the positive test as a sign of an active tuberculosis. Beyond seven or eight years of age many children (25 to 40 per cent) of the lower economic strata show a positive test. The decision whether an active process is present must be based on further clinical and X-ray evidence.

With Camille Kereszturi Cayley, who had become a close friend, and with William H. Park, Béla published another paper: "Parenteral BCG Vaccination." Then came two others: "Tubercle Bacilli in the Stomach Content of Children with Positive Tuberculin Test" and "Acid-Fast Bacilli in the Stomach Lavage and Feces of Tuberculous Children." In these last two works, Béla and Camille were aided by doctors David Hauptmann, Lucy Mishulow and Dorothy Behner.

Whenever Béla advanced to a point where he was to attack the problem of another disease, he would note down a mass of questions. These he would set out to solve one by one, if necessary. He did the same with tuberculosis: "What is clinical tuberculosis in childhood? How is the diagnosis of pulmonary tuberculosis established in childhood?" He would use these as headings in his writings: "A clinical classification of pulmonary tuberculosis in childhood. Tuberculin in the diagnosis of tuberculosis. The clinic for tuberculosis in children. The purpose of the clinic if adult tuberculosis is an exogenous reinfection. Therapy, its indications and aims. The role of the preventorium in dealing with tuberculosis. Hospital facilities for the care of tuberculous children."

So Béla attempted to answer question after question, trying to solve the latest riddle, discussing it with other doctors, those who had become engrossed in the same problems because of his suggestions, his guidance, his hints and encouragements. Three hospitals served as the base for his scientific and educational work: Mount Sinai, Sea View and Willard Parker. At the same time he became a regular lecturer at Columbia University as Clinical Professor of Diseases of Children.

As time passed and medicine progressed, over half a dozen other methods of treating tuberculosis were adopted, the most significant being with streptomycin and para-aminosalicylic acid and with isoniazid and streptomycin. Nevertheless the diagnostic methods of Béla Schick remained basic.

CHAPTER TWENTY-ONE

Allergy

EACH YEAR IN THE UNITED STATES OVER 10,000,000 PEOPLE suffer from a strange disease which up to a very short time ago the world did not even recognize as a specific ailment. If it had not been for Béla Schick's innate curiosity, which led him and his friend Clemens von Pirquet into a long train of observations and experiments, there might have been no such disease categorized so soon. But fate decreed that Béla Schick as a premature infant should not die and that Clemens von Pirquet should give up all intention of becoming a Catholic priest and should turn to medicine. Fate decreed that the two should meet, become firm friends and co-scholars, so that in 1905 they could publish the classical monograph on serum disease, a disease later to be named allergy, and to be recognized as a new branch of medicine.

Allergy had attracted the attention of certain groups as an important subject of study in the United States long before Béla Schick's arrival. News of what he and von Pirquet were doing, their discovery of allergy and their development of the knowledge of allergy, had spread out of Vienna and reached American shores. The fact is that Béla, whose interest in the subject continued throughout his entire career, took every opportunity to foster interest in others, especially the younger members of his profession. To illustrate, let us relate the following incident.

One of Béla's associates at Mount Sinai was sadly afflicted with jealousy. Apparently he had hoped to be appointed chief of the Pediatric Department, and he was left with bitterness over Béla's receiving the post. Béla was not at first aware of this but was abruptly made conscious of it when this colleague conducted him on a tour of the hospital to acquaint him with the facilities and with the doctors with whom he would have to work.

On this tour Béla noticed that his guide was completely ignoring some doctors, while belittling the accomplishments of others. One of those slighted was a young doctor, M. Murray Peshkin. Béla had already heard about him and knew he had started the Clinic of Allergy at Mount Sinai Hospital in 1919 and was working in 1923 on the problem of asthma in children. Béla's guide skated over these problems very lightly, ending: "These are only the beginnings, and maybe when Dr. Peshkin becomes more involved with the problem of asthma in children, he will be able to present his findings. Who knows, by that time nothing may come of it. . . ." He took Béla by the arm with the intention of conducting him to another room, saying, "And now, we have many other things to see in the hospital. . . ."

But Béla held back when he saw that young Dr. Peshkin wanted to speak about his work. He pulled his arm out of the clutch of his impatient guide, and turned back to Dr. Peshkin. He wanted to know something about this young man's work in the field of allergy in children.

It was the beginning of a strong friendship between Béla and Dr. Peshkin, or Murray, as Béla called him from that time on.

Béla discovered that young Murray had already published an interesting report on an allergy case, October 23, 1920, entitled "Ipecac Sensitization and Bronchial Asthma." Under Béla's guidance and encouragement Murray Peshkin was to become one of the outstanding allergists in the country, alongside Robert A. Cooke, George Piness and Harold A. Abramson. He was to write over fifty works on various aspects of allergy in children and adults, to be hailed throughout the world in the first rank of noted therapists.

When Béla Schick, one of the founders of the American Academy of Pediatrics, held his first round-table discussion on allergy under the auspices of that institution, he invited Murray to be his assistant. The doctors who took part in the discussion were H. H. Donnelly of Washington, D. C.; Fred W. Lathrop of Plainfield, New Jersey; F. P. Gengenbach of Denver, Colorado; C. E. Bradley, Jr. of Tulsa, Oklahoma; Henry H. Perlman of Philadelphia, Pennsylvania; L. L. Birnberg of St. Paul, Minnesota, and others. The opening remarks of Béla Schick in this discussion display his accurate observations.

> Recent literature contains much discussion about the allergic nature of such a disease as rheumatic infection. This contention is nothing unusual or even striking for it is self-evident. If one speaks of allergic disease per se, then some other meaning is implied. This alludes to the condition of altered reactivity which may be accompanied by such intensive symptoms that an unpleasant and sometimes a dangerous situation occurs. Such an intense reaction is referred to as being an 'hyperergic reaction.'
>
> The hyperergic reaction is also referred to as an anaphylactic shock. A person with asthma, eczema, or some other so-called 'allergic disease' is recognized as suffering with an hyperergic reaction. Allergy really is not a good term for this condition because allergy may exist without hyperergic features.
>
> Allergy is not harmful or dangerous, despite the statements made by Dr. Rich to the contrary. It is the hyperergic reaction that may become dangerous. The patient with asthma or eczema may be hyperergic to a minute amount of foreign substance. Some authors state the condition of allergy is not essential for immunity in tuberculosis. This contention is incorrect. It is the hyperergic reaction that is not necessary, and in fact is even disadvantageous.

Béla went on to show that the studies on serum sickness

which he had carried on with his friend Clemens von Pirquet, and Clemens himself in his work on vaccination, had proved that the hyperergic reaction was not necessary, that in fact it was merely an unpleasant accompaniment of allergy.

> In the case of a first infection with a vaccine, a minute amount of pathogenic virus invades the host. A relatively long incubation period is necessary for the formation of antibodies. The invading germ, meantime, multiplies while the antibodies are being formed in sufficient amount to fight off the invading virus. If the individual possesses antibodies or is capable of forming antibodies quickly, it is a great advantage.

But this was the altered reactivity called "allergy" brought on by the first infection. What about the instance where the person is reinfected or superinfected? In such a case, he explained, the host reacts at once.

> The invading virus is killed off immediately or at least very quickly, so that the amount of pathogenic organisms capable of reacting with the antibodies is very small; in fact, the number of pathogens reacting with the antibodies with the second or later invasions is very much smaller than in the case of the first invasion of the host. This type of allergic reaction in itself is good, but, unfortunately, allergic reactions as a result of overdosage of pathogens are sometimes accompanied by hyperergic reactions, and these latter reactions are harmful to the host.
>
> So far as acute infectious diseases are concerned, hyperergic reactions are rare. In a chronic infectious disease such as tuberculosis, hyperergic reactions commonly occur. It should be emphasized that an hyperergic reaction represents only a small part of the entity referred to as the allergic reaction. Moreover, clinical immunity is based on allergy. Pirquet even favored the idea of considering antitoxic immunity as it occurs in diphtheria on a basis of allergy. Unfortunately, the hyperergic reaction is almost always identified only with

allergy. In order to avoid the confusion, the allergic diseases should really be called 'hyperergic diseases.' The confusion did not originate with the clinician but with the serologist who studied the anaphylactic (hyperergic) reaction in the guinea pig.

Hyperergic reactions occurring in infectious diseases are unpleasant and not desired. We may go further and say that the hyperergic reaction does not belong to immunity. Allergic reactions may bring about immunity but not the hyperergic reaction. We can separate immunity on the one side and hyperergic reaction on the other. Therefore, the treatment of tuberculosis with tuberculin may well be revived. The treatment with old tuberculin is nothing more than a process of hyposensitization. If an individual has a tuberculous focus, he may become hyperergic to tuberculin, and making such an individual hyposensitive may do good.

Returning to the subject of asthma, it can be broadly stated that it is proper and desirable to institute measures which will diminish the sensitiveness of an hyperergic individual. The patient should be sufficiently cared for so that a severe (hyperergic) reaction is avoided when he comes in contact with the offending substance. If a person is sensitive to nuts, it is unwise to inject him with an extract of nuts, for it is much better and simpler to avoid them. It becomes necessary to desensitize (hyposensitize) a person suffering with hay fever when for economic reasons he is unable to migrate to a relatively pollen-free country. In Europe the wealthy people go to Helgoland where they are relieved of hay fever. However, the vast majority of persons with hay fever in Europe, as well as in the United States, cannot afford to spend some weeks in a pollen-free environment, and they are obliged to submit to hyposensitization treatment with specific pollen extracts.

He went on to praise Dr. Peshkin's work as chief of the Clinic for Allergic Diseases at Mount Sinai Hospital, for it was Peshkin who had devised the testing technique that Béla considered the most reliable and at the same time, from the stand-point of the children, the safest.

The scratch method of testing is always done first, and, if the reactions are negative, then the intracutaneous or intradermal method of testing is performed. In the absence of positive reactions to the intradermal tests, especially with the pollens, then the ophthalmic technic is employed. It should be realized that there exists no absolute difference between the three methods of testing. It is merely a matter of concentration of the test material. If you perform a scratch test for tuberculosis, it is permissible to use the concentrated old tuberculin. If, however, you wish to test intracutaneously, then a dilution of tuberculin must be used.

It is true that different persons as well as the same person differ in their clinical response to specific hyper-sensitiveness. Because of this difference in reactivity the clinical manifestations of hyperergia may become localized in a tissue or organ in the body. If the brain is hyperergic, then migraine or epilepsy may develop. If the gastrointestinal tract is involved, vomiting, diarrhea, colic, and other symptoms appear. Hyperergia of the skin results in urticaria, lichen urticatus, and ec-zema. If the respiratory tract is the seat of hyper-ergic activity, symptoms of hay fever or asthma will be observed.

Hyperergic reactivity may be present in more than one organ of the body. For example, asthma and ec-zema frequently occur in a child concurrently or at different times. There also exists some relationship be-tween the different organs of the body. For instance, hypersensitiveness of the respiratory tract can usually be confirmed by means of the protein skin tests. In eczema, and especially in urticaria, it must be con-ceded that the skin tests (scratch and intradermal technics) are not very satisfactory. Even the patch test fre-quently gives disappointing results. As a matter of fact, all methods of testing have their limitations. A negative test does not rule out the offending factor. Posi-tive cutaneous reactions elicited by testing demonstrate only the hyperergic state of the skin. Positive reactions vary in their intensity. The importance of each positive reaction in the etiology of the hyperergic state must be determined individually. Peshkin has shown that (with the scratch test) a very mild reaction (one-plus or plus-minus) may play a more important role in the etiology of hyperergia than the positive reactions of greater intensity.

To begin with, many children have an inherent predisposition to hyperergic reactions, and hyperergic disease may be initiated as a result of various intercurrent conditions. During life the localization of the hyperergic reaction may change and shift. A child starts in infancy with eczema and within one to seven years it may develop asthma. If an infant is sensitive to certain substances with which it has never come in contact, then the work of Ratner regarding the question of sensitization through the placenta during embryonic life must be considered. It is also important to inquire into the diet of the pregnant woman. It is quite possible for the mother to sensitize the child during intrauterine life.

Then Béla concluded, as always in the interests of accuracy, that there is no cure discovered for asthma. The treatment is rather a relief.

The word 'cure' cannot be applied to a condition in which the predisposition to that condition always remains with the patient. We treat the tendency to attacks either by avoiding the offending substances or by the process of hyposensitization. Nature sometimes also institutes her own treatment. Something happens to the constitution of the child, and the tendency to hyperergic reactions is diminished.

A little before this time, Béla had learned of the sad fate of one who had been his closest friend and co-worker, Clemens von Pirquet. Dr. von Pirquet had gone a long way on the path he had chosen. Up to a short time before the tragedy he had built himself up to a position of highest esteem. He had become a national figure, finally selected as a candidate for President of the Republic of Austria. On the surface this was all a success story. Such activities were quite beyond the aims of his friend Béla Schick, who never at any time desired to become identified as a public figure.

But it was different with Clemens von Pirquet. He had a quick, nervous brilliance, not the enduring, inquisitive stubbornness of a Béla Schick. Clemens was something of a crusader. He had involved himself deeply into the problems of social medicine because of his impatience to lead others into an improved state of living. But while he was getting things done, his perpetual impatience left him no peace, no real sense of satisfaction. There were other disturbing factors in his life also. The protracted illness of his wife, Maria, the lawsuit brought against him by his own brother-in-law, Professor Eiselsberg, involving a claim of five thousand dollars. Perhaps hardest to bear was the sense of dissatisfaction and remorse that engulfed him because in devoting his energies to social medicine he had been forced gradually to abandon his scientific endeavors. Out of the laboratory came the lasting sense of achievement. Out of all his public campaigning he gained only applause and flattery. Had he betrayed something truly great within him? When his candidacy for President of his country was suddenly dropped, everything seemed empty. He was only in the fifty-fifth year of his life. But he had staked so much on success. Now defeat was unbearable.

Three months passed. His devoted Maria helped him to make the supreme decision between life and death. He chose what was to him a comfortable way out. Both he and his wife committed suicide by consuming cyanide of potassium.

Von Pirquet's assistant, Dr. Nobel, at once cabled the tragic news to Béla in New York. Béla wept as he would have done at the death of his own father or his only brother. But work for Béla was the real salvation. He sat down and wrote a three-thousand word article full of praise for the medical genius of the departed man, and sent it to the Berlin periodical *Zeitschrift Für Kinderheilkunde.*

Then he resolutely returned to his main task, the advancement of the knowledge of disease, the banishment of disease from the world. He campaigned for this alone. His work was in the laboratory, in investigation and discovery, and in the creation of a new generation inspired with the same zeal and knowledge as himself.

Dr. Peshkin, in a talk with the author of this book, stated with fervor: "Béla gave me, as he gave to so many other American and European allergists, the foundations for scientific work. He nourished me. He showed me how to examine, diagnose, how to cure. Without his help, and without his encouragement, I would have been nothing. At the most I would have been one of the thousands of ordinary general practitioners."

Such earnest, overwhelming gratitude is typical of most of Béla's students and associates, and throughout his long and enriching career he had several thousand of them.

During the course of a discussion that the author had with Béla Schick on the problem of allergy, the doctor handed him a manuscript with the ink still fresh.

"Place this somewhere in your book," he said.

The title of the manuscript was "Allergy, Your Friend or Enemy." Half of it was hand-written by his devoted Cathy; the second section was in Béla's own hand-writing. In simple sentences, much as he spoke, the indefatigable Béla discusses allergy in everyday life. This is one of his latest papers on the subject, addressed to children but understandable to everybody; and here is how his thoughts run.

> I feel sure that, during the summer, when many of you are enjoying the country in the midst of meadows, trees and flowers, you have a friend who feels utterly miserable due to sneezing, a running nose, and difficulty of breathing (caused by asthma or hay fever).
>
> If the hay fever is severe enough, your friend may be sent to Bethlehem in the White Mountains, because it is free of ragweed. Or perhaps you have a brother, sister or schoolmate who cannot eat strawberries or raspberries though loving them. If they should eat them, they would break out with a rash, called hives,

and suffer from a terrible itching. You, on the other hand, may be able to eat these delicious berries and suffer no ill effects.

If you go to a summer camp, they will probably warn you not to touch poison ivy because you may be sensitive to it, and if this is the case you would develop a very annoying rash causing itching, swelling and pain lasting for days. Other children you may have known run into trouble if they play with a dog, cat, rabbit, horse or other animal. If they go horseback riding, they may get an asthma attack and hardly be able to breathe.

Why can you play with all these animals without getting any of these unpleasant and even dangerous symptoms?

Or it may be that you have a brother or sister who got scarlet fever, diphtheria or mumps. Your parents feared you might also get the disease, but, lo and behold, you remained perfectly well in spite of the fact that you played with them and even kissed and hugged them. What is the explanation? Why this difference? Why do you get measles only once in your life? And why do doctors give babies injections with needles? Your mother will tell you that they do it to protect you against certain diseases like diphtheria, tetanus, whooping cough and smallpox.

You see, everybody does not get diphtheria or scarlet fever, etc. Something in the body must be different in different persons. It must be that some people have something that protects them against these diseases. In the case of asthma and hives, the fact that something is present in the body brings about these conditions. Thus, some children can eat what they like, play with animals and touch everything without getting into trouble, whereas other children cannot.

Many diseases are due to microbes (germs or virus). These microbes invade our body like enemy soldiers might invade a country. Inside our body they multiply and manufacture a poison which makes us sick. Very soon billions of microbes are in our body, so in order to survive, our body produces a substance which make the poison harmless.

This substance appears in the watery part of the blood called the serum and brings the disease to an end. The serum contains these protective substances for a long time after the disease is over. Thus, if the same kind of germ or virus should attack us again, it would be destroyed by these substances without doing us any harm.

In other diseases, the germs multiply without producing a poison, but if nothing were to be done about them they would multiply to such an extent that the blood in the blood vessel would not be able to move. And so the body must produce substances which will kill off the germs as quickly as possible. By killing the germs, poisonous substances in the germs are set free and it is this which makes us sick.

After all the germs are killed, the disease comes to an end. Those beneficial substances stay in our body and if we are again exposed to the same germs, we are able to kill them off quickly without getting sick. That is what is meant when we say we are 'immune.' Thus, becoming immune to certain diseases, we get them only once in a lifetime. Even if we eventually lose these protecting substances in our serum, our system has not forgotten how to manufacture them. We are able to do it more quickly than the first time, and so the germs have no time to do us any harm.

Because of this you can see that a person who had a certain disease before is different from a person who never had the disease. The reaction of the body to the invasion of germs has changed. This altered reaction is called allergy. Thus certain diseases make us 'allergic.' This form of allergy is good for us and is our friend because it keeps us healthy.

When the doctor injects children with 'needles' he produces a very mild disease in the child in order to force the body system to manufacture the same protecting substances as are manufactured when the child actually has the disease. In this way the child is immunized.

There are other substances which can make us sick. We know that if we inject a horse with the poison of the diphtheria germ, we force the horse to manufacture the same substance which we produce to make the diphtheria poison harmless. With the 'serum' of such horses, we cure children who are sick with diphtheria and save their lives. Unfortunately, the serum of a horse is different from our serum. It is a foreign substance, called a foreign protein. Our body does not permit such a foreign substance to remain in us. Thus we destroy it by a kind of digestion like we destroy foreign 'proteins' present in meat or eggs which we eat. These substances in our food are digested in our stomachs and in the bowels and in this way prepared for our body without any difficulty or symptoms of any sickness.

Our stomach and bowels have digestive substances which break down the protein to the so-called 'aminoacids' which we absorb. These aminoacids are the bricks with which our own protein can be rebuilt for our own use. This breaking down of foreign protein is accomplished without difficulty and without symptoms of any disease.

It is not so if one injects the serum of a horse under the skin. Digestive substances are not present in the serum and have to be manufactured, and appear only after 8 to 12 days. These substances do not work as perfectly as those in the stomach and bowels. Poisonous intermediary substances are produced which are absorbed and make us sick. We then break out with hives and have fever and other symptoms of 'serum-sickness.' Just as in the above-mentioned disease, these substances (called 'antibodies') remain in our serum for several months. If we should be forced to inject horse serum a second time, the destruction of the horse serum starts immediately, and poisonous intermingling substances appear rapidly. Sometimes the hives appear almost immediately after injection. We see that the reaction to the second injection is altered. This person is *allergic* to horse serum. The symptoms of serum disease may be more intensive and may be not only hives but similar to those of an intensive asthma attack.

These facts led to the discovery that hives and asthma are due to foreign protein substances existing in strawberries, raspberries, fish, eggs, oysters, pollen of different grasses (e.g. ragweed) or protein present in emanations coming from animals (horses, cats, dogs, feathers from birds, chickens, ducks, geese), in molds, in the house dust or furniture, and hundreds of other sources including bacteria, virus, new drugs (like penicillin, streptomycin, sulfa drugs, etc.) inhaling such substances into our lungs may produce asthmatic attacks.

Those who get hives or asthmatic attacks we call allergic to the different substances. Some people get hives and varied rashes by touching or by being in contact with these substances. Skin lesions like eczema develop upon an allergic basis. In the serum of such allergic persons we find such substances (antibodies) just mentioned. By testing, we can determine to which proteins the person is allergic. You can imagine how badly off a person must be who is sensitive to pollen or ragweed in the air or to the dust in the house.

If one is sensitive (allergic) to certain foodstuffs like chocolate, nuts or berries, the best treatment is not to eat them. It is more difficult for persons allergic to ragweed to avoid inhaling pollen.

Therefore many such sufferers are healed with injections of pollen extracts, which desensitize the patient against pollen or ragweed or other grasses. It is easy to see that these substances producing hives and asthma are not our friends. Allergy against pollen is very disturbing and is decidedly an enemy of our wellbeing.

But it must be said that as our health is more endangered by germs and viruses, allergy is a real friend and the only means of saving us from disease and death. Therefore, we should be happy and thankful that allergy exists. Allergy's beneficial aspects outweigh by far its inimical side.

CHAPTER TWENTY-TWO

Different People, Different Places

AMONG THE YOUNGER MEMBERS OF THE PROFESSION HELPED BY Béla Schick was Samuel Karelitz. He was the discovery of that illustrious American scholar and scientist, Béla's friend, Edwards A. Park. This remarkable young student of Dr. Park's was twenty-three when Béla came upon him at Mount Sinai Hospital. Béla's innate sense for searching out genius caused him to concentrate on young Sam. Sam was a "bright boy," Béla said. Sam was able to say later and with great pride, "I was resident pediatrician under Dr. Schick between 1923 and 1927." Indeed, Béla encouraged him and watched over him as if he were his own son. And Sam added, "He helped me to get an Emanuel Libman fellowship to study abroad. . . . So I studied in 1926 with Finkelstein, Czerny, Pirquet and Ludwig Pick."

From that time on, the development of Sam Karelitz, who invented among other things the continuous intravenous drip, gained him reputation as a brilliant clinician and therapist until he had become one of the most eminent pediatricians in America.

"I have written," Sam told the author of this book, "some seventy-five articles on pediatric problems, mainly in connection with infectious diseases, treatment of diarrhea, serum sickness, and several chapters in text books, etc. . . . I have confirmed experimentally the Schick theory of serum sickness, which others had challenged."

This was Béla's way. He was always looking for talent, discovering, encouraging, assisting his protégés, obtaining for them scholarships, fellowships, stipends, allowances of one sort or another. The main thing was that these young students be given the opportunity to devote as much time as possible to their studies, journey to Europe for further work, deepening and comparing the acquired knowledge of the New World with the Old. For Béla never forgot his own struggles as a student, how often he had to do work that kept him away from worthwhile study, and he knew that not every student could stand this perpetual grind.

Béla himself travelled to Europe practically every year to exchange ideas with European scientists and to visit his mother, his brother and sisters. He would return from these trips with a multitude of ideas that would enable him to solve technical and administrative problems in the hospitals where he worked, together with novel therapeutic approaches, which he would carefully test in the children's wards.

Unfortunately post-Versailles Europe, Béla noticed, was undergoing rapid change, and all for the worse. The market for gainful employment decreased. Production in many places was at a standstill. The number of unemployed grew by leaps and bounds. The cost of living was hopelessly rising. So the ground was made fertile for hates and animosities, for the Mussolinis and the Hitlers. All helping to start a new armaments race and eventually a new World War.

Béla traveled about, making his own observations. In the summer of 1935, he visited the Soviet Union a second time to attend the International Physiological Congress, and remarked "that the majority of the people carried on without luxuries, even without what we are wont to consider necessities in this blessed land of ours. All this so that heavy industry might be prepared when war would come. . . ." He noticed too, "the tremendous enthusiasm for medical and scientific research encountered everywhere in Russia" which "impressed me very much."

On the way home, Béla Schick was entertained in Poland by the Polish Pediatric Society, headed by Dr. Michalowicz and Dr. F. Groer, the latter being a close acquaintance of Béla's from Vienna days. Schick, Groer and Michalowicz, among others, edited one of the most profound and scholarly international reviews of pediatrics, entitled *Annales Paediatrici.*

His Polish friends gave Béla a grim and pessimistic picture of the growth of chauvinism in Europe, which resulted in nothing of merit—only dictatorships and war.

Two years later, Béla visited the Near East, where he acquainted himself with the life of the Arabs and the Jews in Palestine. He was astonished to find that the Jews had been able to lower the infant mortality rate to 5 per cent. Commenting on this, Béla said, "In Austria, which enjoyed a splendid reputation for its highly developed medical knowledge, a 12 to 15 per cent infant mortality rate existed before the First World War. During my first visit to Mexico in 1936, I was informed that the mortality rate of Indian children up to ten years of age amounted to the incredible figure of 70 per cent, which means that the mother giving birth to ten children will see only three survive to be ten years of age. Only since the new government of Mexico instituted an intensive campaign against the ravages caused by childhood diseases has great improvement been accomplished."

Returning to the subject of the Jews, he continued, "I am sure that even the Arabs would admit that the blessings of medical science were brought to them only through the immigration of Jewish physicians, scientists and workers. Malaria, trachoma, dysentery, skin ailments, as well as other diseases would have continued their fateful courses as they did before the advent of the Jews, and thousands of Arabs who are now alive and healthy would have suffered and died. Epidemic diseases have no respect for the homes of the rich, no respect for race, creed or color. Disease germs are the real international enemies of mankind." After a moment of deliberation, he added, "The pediatrician, of course, cannot devote his time only to the prevention of disease but must also consider the harmonic development of body and mind, which has been greatly facilitated by our present knowledge. The foundation for the future cannot be laid early enough. Raising healthy children is the best prenatal care for the children of the future father and mother."

The development and promotion of medicine was the single interest of Béla Schick, who preferred to ignore politics and differences in ideologies. He was able to remain impartial because of this undivided interest, even though his constant traveling made him much aware of the changes taking place in the world around him. He returned to the United States full of his observations about the outstanding advances in medicine in each of the countries he visited. And people listened and learned from him, honored and awarded him. The changes going on in the world, running towards their crises, had no effect on his wholly preoccupied life.

On March 3, 1938 at the New York Academy of Medicine, whose president at that time was Dr. James A. Miller, a banquet was held in observance of the twenty-fifth anniversary of the discovery of the Schick test. Several hundred doctors, scientists and educators attended, from the United States, Europe, Mexico and Canada. The central attractions were Béla Schick and his Cathy.

Among those present was his close companion from Vienna, Dr. Karl Landsteiner, a pathologist who just eight years before had received the Nobel Prize for classifying human blood in different types. Cathy's parents were there, and Béla's countless friends, acquaintances and former students from various hospitals in New York and from the entire country.

The setting was festive, and the guests of honor, Béla and Cathy, stole glances at each other, rather like two children caught out at some mischief and awaiting punishment from their parents.

In presenting the Academy of Medicine Gold Medal, Dr. Miller reviewed Béla's career in pediatrics, referring particularly to the development of the Schick test, and declared:

> Your place, therefore, is among the great benefactors of mankind.
> This is a well deserved honor. Since you received your medical degree in 1900 at the Karl Franz University at Graz, Austria, you have devoted your energies

not only to clinical medicine but also to medical investigation and to teaching.

As early as 1905 you, with Clemens von Pirquet, also a distinguished pupil of Theodor Escherich, published the classical monograph *Serumkrankheit*. This not only gave the first description of serum sickness, but also established fundamental principles of allergy. In 1912, with Escherich, you published the celebrated clinical monograph on scarlet fever. You had meanwhile promulgated the idea that post-scarlatinal diseases were allergic in nature. This is now a firmly established fact, of wide significance.

You have also made important studies of the nutrition of the newborn, of infantile tuberculosis, of metabolism in infectious diseases, as well as of other subjects.

It was in 1913, that you published the discovery which has given you the widest fame—the reaction which so justly carries your name. This was no chance observance, but was the result of careful studies carried on over a number of years.

Through this discovery you made it possible to determine who is and who is not susceptible to diphtheria, and this laid the basis for the present-day effective campign of prevention against this dreaded disease. . . .

But Béla wanted to bring in other names, for he felt as always that no credit belongs to one man alone, and he replied in his acceptance speech, "That my work could be instrumental in accomplishing so much for the community is naturally a source of great satisfaction to me, but I know that my test could only have been discovered on the basis of the discoveries of Pirquet, that genius in medicine, and I am also aware of the fact that my test would not have been so quickly accepted if not for the splendid work of Dr. William H. Park and his co-workers, particularly the late Dr. Abraham Zingher. I might add that my professional work has been inspired by the great Pasteur's statement. . . ." And Béla quoted his favorite passage, the utterance of man's faith that all diseases can be wiped off the face of the earth.

Meanwhile, on April 12th of the same year, Béla received in absentia the British award, the Addingham Gold Medal, for "the most valuable discovery for relieving pain and suffering in humanity." The last recipient had been Sir Henry Hallett Dale of London, co-winner with Professor Otto Loewi of Vienna of the Nobel Prize in Medicine and Physiology in 1936 for his pioneer discoveries of the chemical activity of nerve impulses.

W. H. Clarke, solicitor for the trustees of the estate of Hoffman Wood, who established this medal, wrote to Béla Schick on that same day: "We think it only proper to mention that at the ceremony of presentation, Sir Henry Hallett Dale made the most complimentary remarks about your work, and indeed about you personally, and expressed the personal view that the trustees had made a most wise decision in awarding the medal to you. We thought you would welcome intimation to this effect from so eminent a medical man as Sir Henry Hallett Dale."

It was proof that the results of medical research and discovery transcended national boundaries. Medical benefits to one nation meant the same benefits to any other nation. Or so Béla reasoned. But was it true? The people of his own faith were being persecuted in Germany. Could he go on ignoring that? Could he ignore the fact that brutality and ruthlessness were being practiced against scholars, authors, artists, regardless of their achievements, regardless of how much they had done for mankind?

The climax for Béla came on one of his visits to "sunny" Italy. Both he and his wife were ejected from their hotel to make room for a company of German Nazis, who could not live under the same roof with a Jew. Finally, the occupation of Austria destroyed all Béla's illusions, when he heard of the destruction, the murder, the suicide of so many prominent physicians he counted amoung his friends.

When Béla journeyed to Tampa, Florida, on May 20, 1938, to deliver a lecture at the invitation of Dr. Arthur Logie, head

of the Tuberculosis Division of the State Board of Health, he
burst out in bitterness,

> The Spanish Inquisition was no worse than the cur-
> rent destruction of hope in Europe today. Many of the
> doctors who committed suicide after the recent annexa-
> tion of Austria were my friends. I understand why they
> did it.
> Most of the doctors were too old to start rebuild-
> ing a new life even if the opportunity had been left
> open to them. When a man is a doctor, it is some-
> times easy for him to see the futility of life.
> The tragedies of current diplomacy are as distress-
> ing as any in the history of the world.

He still did not realize that what had come upon the world,
like a festering sore, had nothing in common with diplomacy.
How could Béla, so wholly taken up with his professional work,
understand what even the foremost politicians could not understand—that the world was suddenly faced with a species
of international gangsterism?

The record of a single week out of Béla's life at this time
may show how absorbed he was in medical concerns, every
hour of the day. Dr. Logie had invited him to Jacksonville,
Florida, to campaign against tuberculosis by lecturing before
various medical and laymen's societies. This is how the week
went by: Monday, May 16th, in Miami; Tuesday, May 17th, in
West Palm Beach; Wednesday in Lakeland; Thursday in St.
Petersburg; Friday in Tampa; Saturday in Orlando. And on the
following day the return trip by automobile with his wife to
New York City, where his responsibilities awaited him in three
hospitals, private consultations, from which he lived, as well as
welfare and social obligations which mainly consisted of helping Austrian and German intellectuals of Jewish ancestry, who
were just barely able to escape the Nazi terror, and who found
themselves in America or in one of the free countries of Europe.

Cathy was founder and a devoted worker in many of these
organizations, among them the Friends of German Refugees.
She spent entire days and nights visiting acquaintances, soliciting,

corresponding, arranging lectures, banquets, dinners, exhibitions and programs, all for the benefit of the victims of Nazism. Among these victims were noted students and writers, people from all levels of education, up to recipients of the Nobel Prize.

Upon the greying head of Béla fell a new tragedy. On January 12, 1939, his mother passed away in her eightieth year. During her last years she had been living with her youngest daughter, Ilona, in the little Austrian town of Peggau, not far from Graz. Béla had been sending her aid regularly from the United States and had visited her almost every year. Ilona had devotedly tended her mother, dressing her, bathing her, feeding her, and spending every free moment with the enfeebled woman, and at the end it was Ilona who closed her eyelids.

In the last year of Janka's life, Béla had been unable to visit her, for he was barred by the Austrian Nazis. That year was indeed a hard one for Béla. In September, when Hitler's Germany attacked defenseless Poland, Béla learned of the death of Richard, his brother. Soon after this the Nazis placed his sister Frieda in jail. She was subsequently moved from one concentration camp to another, until the end came for her three years later. During the war, over thirty members of Béla's immediate and distant family died in the German concentration camps. Their sole crime was that they had been born to the Jewish faith.

With the coming of the war, Béla allowed himself to be called on for any extra work intended for the common good. He redoubled his free services in the hospitals. He placed himself at the beck and call of governmental agencies such as the State Department, the Department of Justice, and of the welfare and community organizations such as the Red Cross, and the United Hospital Campaign Committee. It was his share in the struggle against racial oppressions and against physical illness.

But as always, Béla kept on with his scientific duties. During the war, he delivered with Dr. Bella Singer an engrossing paper on thoracoplasty in children. This was the result of a ten-year study of various forms of surgery on children suffering with tuberculosis.

Another work was entitled "A Case of Neurofibromatosis in a Child of 5¾ Years of Age." This is a generalized disease involving nervous tissue, in which tumors, frequently multiple, arise from the sheaths of the spinal and cranial nerves and produce symptoms by pressure on neighboring organs. A second characteristic of the disease is the presence of an area of yellow or brown pigmentation scattered over the skin. The prognosis for life in this disease is relatively poor. Intracranial lesions are serious on account of their location and because they are almost always multiple and cannot be completely removed.

Still another of his absorbing works, with doctors Ralph Howard Brodsky and Hermann Vollmer, was entitled "Prevention of Dental Caries by Massive Doses of Vitamin D."

Béla continued prolonged studies of edema in starvation and in nephrosis, where he proved the relationship between edema and hypoproteinemia, which in both cases is the result of lack or loss of protein in the body. These studies related to the slaughter of children in war.

Here are his remarks to the Committee on Child Care of the World Jewish Congress, of which he was a member:

> Starvation alone kills few children. It doesn't have time to kill them. Instead it opens the way for the death-dealing intrusion of other diseases and chief among these is tuberculosis.
>
> Children have marvelous recuperative powers, but they must be helped instantly. Proper food, considerably above the present allotment of 1,500 calories, vitamins and medical attention, given now, at this period of crisis in their lives, is worth five times the amount given a year or two years from now, when, if relief is delayed, they will be victims of many of the dread diseases of childhood.
>
> Leaders in the field of child psychiatry should be sent abroad, not to treat, but to instruct local agencies there in the therapeutic measures necessary to adjust these children to a normal environment, something they

have not had for years. Here in America we are so concerned over the effect of a startling experience on children in their early years, like the death of a pet dog. Just think what it must have meant to them in Europe to see their own parents murdered in front of them.

At best, many of these children will be stunted in growth, retarded in education and warped in their approach to human beings. Once we have taken care of their physical needs adequately, we must supply the means in a normal home atmosphere for them to catch up on the many things they have missed. This will require a special program of education and child welfare, a program which is the concern not only of the government of the country in which they live, but of humanity throughout the world.

No one could know the problem better than Béla, he who had after the First World War brought three shiploads of starving Austrian children down the Danube to Hungary, where he helped personally to care for them for several months in the hope of saving their lives. It was Béla Schick who had almost single-handed organized this project. He had sought for aid himself, and he had had to save the children by his own initiative.

Béla explains that one has to see the effects of war on children with one's own eyes, as he did, to get a true picture of what horrible destruction and devastation war is capable of. The tragedy of war involves not only those children who die as a direct result, but possibly even more those who are starving, injured, crippled and half alive, who must exist in the ruins. What hope of normal development could they have?

To build a better world, a healthier world, a more fortunate one, Béla reasoned, there must be peace. War saps the energies and inventive genius of men. It channels his creative capacities toward one vast dead end—not toward better life for all, but toward quicker death for as many as possible. Although Béla had already passed his sixtieth birthday he labored with unflagging enthusiasm and effort for this ideal world without war.

In January 1941 he was the guest of honor at the annual Forum of Allergy in Indianapolis, Indiana, where he was presented with the Gold Medal for his pioneer work in the field of allergy. An incident on the way to this convention can be cited as further illustration of Béla Schick's essential peacefulness and kindliness, even under considerable provocation.

He was travelling by car. Cathy, an expert driver, was driving along a Pennsylvania highway when they were hit by another car. Both suffered slight concussion, but Béla was the first to leave the car and to help his wife out. The young driver of the other car, overwhelmed with fright, began to offer desperate apologies. But Béla first examined his wife. Finding no injuries, he turned to the young man and asked, "Have you any hatred of doctors?" The young man was taken aback by such a strange question. After a moment's thought he said, "Since you mentioned it, I'll tell you sincerely that I have, in a way. One doctor performed an operation on me. But it turned out to be quite unnecessary."

"Then why do you want to kill me for that? I'm only a pediatrician. And on the other hand, the automobile, that interesting invention, shouldn't be the weapon for deathly revenge."

Béla stepped into his car with Cathy, and they drove away taking no action against the young driver.

On the following day the nation's press reported the incident, and one paper commenting on the black eye sustained as a result of the accident headlined the story: "DR. SCHICK TOTES MEDAL AND SHINER."

CHAPTER TWENTY-THREE

Garrison, N. Y.

IF WORK IS THE SECRET OF PERPETUAL YOUTH, THEN BÉLA SCHICK has that secret. Most men who are advancing along in the sixties begin to reason with themselves it is time to slow up with shorter hours of labor, longer hours of relaxation. But Béla could never think in those terms. He has always liked work, and has always had to work harder and longer each day than most men. Then, too, he has never been really sick. As we have seen, the only operation he had in his life was a quite unnecessary one.

As a man in his sixties his hair was growing whiter, but he still had that quick way of walking, and his face, with the large brown eyes afire with zeal and enthusiasm, presented the picture of a man bursting with ideas, packed with energy for ever further creative work. He was no "health addict" but during the four seasons of the year he constantly walked outdoors without an overcoat, without a hat and without rubbers, most of the time wearing only light summer clothing. In the country he would wear shorts more often than not.

The whole of life was a constant source of enjoyment to Béla Schick. Apart from certain technicalities in hospital rules, there was no reason to believe that there would be any slackening off in his work at his three hospitals, his laboratories and clinics, in addition to his private practise.

So many younger doctors who have come to know Dr. Schick closely have commented on the extraordinary elasticity and clarity of mind which characterizes his answer to any question whether on medical or general matters. Dr. Dan Holbrooke has recalled his first meeting with Béla in 1940, when Béla was sixty-three. Holbrooke was a junior assistant in Béla's department, and since he had invented a non-slip bandage he wanted to show it to Dr. Schick, whom he had not yet met. The great man was in his office in the Pediatric Department. "I must admit," said Dan Holbrooke, "I was a little nervous before this interview, realizing that I was about to meet a very prominent name in the history of medicine, a man about whom I had studied just a few years ago and whose name was an examination subject." But the atmosphere was different in Béla's office. The warm look on Béla's face put everything to rights. Dan found no difficulty in saying what he had to say, for Béla gave all his attention, directed his mind entirely to the merits of the invention, and gave Dan great encouragement. By all means Dan must pursue this work further.

It was a happy experience for Dan, as similar meetings had been for so many other young people doctors. "Later on I learned," said Dan Holbrooke, "that that was his attitude to anything of merit presented to him. He would give all the support, attention and encouragement he could to anybody."

It was part of Béla's philosophy, which he was perfectly willing to explain to anyone. A man who comes to him with a problem, he reasons, has given much of his time and study to it. The positive nature of the problem may not be at once apparent, but always something has caused it to come up. There has been some significant incentive to find a solution. Out of all this there is sure to come something of value.

Dr. Dan Holbrooke expressed it beautifully when he said of Béla: "Dr. Schick is one of the unusual chiefs who create a climate for the ideas to grow. While there are other chiefs of departments who by their stern and impersonal attitude freeze people's ideas for many years to come and dwarf attempts at development, he creates the temperature for the scientific garden, giving the gentle rays to the smallest bud of scientific ideas. This naturally not without a great deal of humor mixed with his deep and serious attitude."

He recalled how one of Béla's assistants came into the office apologizing for disturbing the chief, and proceeded to explain a new theory. "But what is your problem?" Béla asked. "The problem is," explained the young doctor, "shall I or shall I not dare publish my theory?"

Béla looked at him smiling, "By all means publish it." Then he explained, added, "You see, there are only two possibilities. The first is that you may be right. Then the chances are that with the advancement of science ten years from now you will be proven wrong. The second is that you are wrong from the beginning. That is, you are ahead of your time."

Béla would never reject completely any idea expressed to him, no matter how much he disagreed with its author. There was the time when a certain doctor described a cure for asthma performed in some province in India. To most medical minds it clearly fell into the category of necromancy. On a certain day at a monastery hundreds of asthmatics would gather, and during the full moon would look for certain vegetation, while they prayed and received the guidance of the monks. For cure, it was said, the herbs had to be taken during a full moon, brewed in a complicated manner and drunk before sunrise. It was the doctor's theory that once a year this particular herb contained an active principle against asthma; he rejected the possibility of a psychogenic cure.

When the doctor had left, young Dan Holbrooke expressed amazement that a trained M.D. could believe in such lies.

Béla showed surprise, and replied in characteristic manner. "In every lie there may be some truth, and in every truth there is some lie. One has to investigate to establish how much there is of each. This is the function of a scientist." Béla's eyes twinkled as he added, "Myself, I don't believe him either, but I would like to get some of those herbs and try them out without the moon and the monks."

In the autumn of 1942, since he had passed his sixty-fifth birthday, under the rules of the hospital Béla Schick was compelled to resign from the directorship of the Pediatric

Department at Mount Sinai Hospital, and Dr. Murray H. Bass, younger by five years, replaced him. On October 13th of that year, Dr. Schick was elected to the post of consulting pediatrician in acknowledgment of the fact that he had been so instrumental in building up the department to the one most famous in its field in America, and possibly in the entire world.

Béla received the title of consulting pediatrician with gratitude, for no man in the medical world felt less like retiring from so thriving an institution than did Béla. In terms of energy and intense interest he could have carried on the work as chief for another twenty years.

Through the course of twenty years in this distinguished hospital, in so important a position, some people reason that Béla must have made a great deal of money. But this is far from the truth. For the entire period he received the total of eight thousand dollars, which was paid him during the first year of his directorship. After that Béla had to live on his earnings from private practice and from consultations, whenever other physicians called on his aid in complicated cases.

In his new position of consulting pediatrician he had to visit Mount Sinai Hospital fairly frequently, perhaps to see a private patient, to use the laboratory, or for a hospital case. But due to the presence of new personnel, it happened once or twice that Béla was not recognized, or that through some undercurrent of jealousy he found himself treated without the respect due him. Such situations are experienced by all consultant physicians at one time or another, and only amused Béla. He had a plan, he said, for every doctor who reached the age of sixty-five and was about to leave the hospital. "He should purchase a handsome, pedigreed dog a few weeks before he is to leave, and should acquaint the dog with the hospital personnel and with the physicians. A dog is naturally loved by everybody from the very beginning. Without fail, this doctor should come each day with the dog and show him to everyone from the president of the hospital on down to the lowliest kitchen employee."

Those who heard the suggestion at once asked why.

"Because, when that doctor becomes consultant he won't find it necessary to identify his legitimacy with a host of certificates, documents and papers to every individual to prove that he had spent many, many years in the hospital in a directorship and that he should have admittance even now without any boundaries or limits and without some person turning up his nose at him. Any person could recognize the pedigreed dog, and after that even his master."

When the burst of laughter subsided, he added in his customarily easy manner, "Isn't it true, though, that most people prefer dogs or other animals to their own next of kin?"

But Béla never had to take these little occurrences seriously, for no doctor was more popular than Béla Schick. Béla loved people. He loved to listen to their ideas, to encourage them. He demanded the best from those around him, but above all he knew how to make them want to give him their best work. Of nurses he said, "A good nurse in a hospital is a foundation for a good hospital." He appreciated even the smallest physical task done on his behalf, whether by some fellow physician or some servant or the cook that had dished up the potatoes. He had respect for a man's work, respect for his position, and respect for his name.

Whenever Béla was forced to leave some hospital position, the farewell ceremony was made distinctive by the fact that the nursing section gave a spontaneous expression of sorrow at his departure. To them Béla had been a co-worker and a father, and tears would come to their eyes at the thought of his leaving.

How they felt can be deduced from the song composed for him at the farewell gathering at Mount Sinai; no masterpiece of art, but what better expression of genuine feeling?

> Oh, Dr. Schick, how we will miss you!
> Oh, Béla Schick, good luck we wish you!
> To your happy future way
> We rise and sing today
> In reverence, for inspiration,
> Guidance and fair play.
> Oh, Dr. Schick, we all salute you
> With affection in our hearts

Since you've come across the ocean
You have earned our full devotion.
Hail to Béla Schick!

And while on the subject of simple songs, let there be added a biographical sketch of Béla written during the days of his directorship at Mount Sinai Hospital by his metabolism specialist Dr. Anne Topper, member of the hospital "harem" as well as close personal friend of Cathy. Sereral times at small gatherings of friends Béla was forced into taking his place at the piano while Anne would sing to the tune of "When I was a lad" from *H.M.S. Pinafore*:

When I was a lad in Hungary
I couldn't dance the czardas, or the bokonee,
My dancing had so many faults,
They sent me to Vienna to learn to waltz.
At waltzing I achieved such fame,
That assistant to von Pirquet I soon became.
To von Pirquet I felt so inferior,
I decided to investigate diphtheria.
I diligently pursued my quest,
Till quite by accident I found a new skin test.
The test it was named after me,
And that's why I received so much publicity.

My fame soon spread across the sea,
To Mt. Sinai where there was a vacancy.
There were many good men on the spot,
But since they wanted glamor, the job I got.
They made me head of the children's ward
And many of the things I found there, I deplored.

In the kitchen I found such extravagant waste,
The garbage was enough to feed another place.
So what do you think I gave them?
That marvelous discovery the N.E.M.
This system plus cooperative men
Enabled me to travel now and then.

I went back to Europe every year
But always damn happy to come back here,
Then came the war, and I couldn't go abroad,
So I traveled in America in my old Ford.
But what with priorities in Texaco,
I couldn't even travel to Mexico

And so I decided to buy a farm,
And spend my days in ease and charm,
Traveling became so embarrassin'
I was lucky to find a house in Garrison.
And there in my mountain greenery,
I intended to retire amid the scenery.

Well, Anne Topper will be remembered for her work as a physician! She also was quite accurate in her allusion to Garrison.

About fifty miles out of New York City in Putnam County is the railroad station of Garrison. The village consists of little more than a general store and a few houses. In April 1941, Béla and Cathy bought a 26-acre piece of land with an old five-room house on one end of the property, and on the other end a somewhat newer seven-room house with a henhouse alongside. The entire expanse of land covered by trees and bushes is cut by two country roads, which are very seldom used by anybody. The nearest neighbor is about a mile away in forest-covered hills.

For the mailman the estate is the last stop, and for Béla and Cathy it is the beginning of country life where they spend each free moment together.

Most of their time there, the Schicks stay at the larger house, a white house with large rooms, furnished with early American furniture. Their love of antiques is shown in the smaller articles that cover the bureaus, dressers, shelves and tables, and even the window sills.

There are old American jugs, as well as Bennington pottery, twelve Staffordshire dogs, ironstone China, sixty trivets, and an interesting pewter collection. The shelves are full of books and the walls are hung with original paintings and reproductions of

the masters. One can see that all of this is solicitously cared for by Cathy, and the entire house on the inside looks like some sort of local museum.

In addition to running water, gas, telephone and radio, the house has four major attractions: extremely comfortable beds, a modern kitchen, a television set, and a large up-to-date bathroom, the walls papered with designs of unusual fish.

From the outside, the house would seem to be growing out of a hillside covered with bushes that flower in the spring, and with rambling roses. From the west, the hill hides the house so that it cannot be seen until one is almost on top of it, passing along the country road to the east. The fragrance of lilacs, honeysuckle, iris, peonies, daffodils, and wild violets fills the air.

At the north side of the house is the entrance to the kitchen by a narrow path, but at the south side is a large screened veranda running the entire length of the house, where one can sit in a comfortable chair to watch the group of children bathing in the swimming pool. For there is a green shimmering tiled pool, and there are children. These children are the lucky ones from New York City, who have been invited to stay with the Schicks for the summer.

During the summer the children, with Béla and Cathy, swim in the pool, then spread themselves out on the surrounding lawn to eat a simple and delicious meal cooked on the open stove which stands in the garden.

The former henhouse up under the hill has been remodeled into a modernistic, expansive one-room studio, with a couch, table, chairs, dresser, bookcase and an old-fashioned huge iron pot-bellied stove. At times the Schicks hide away here, when they want to escape from their numerous guests. But usually this is the lodging of some guest who is rather exceptionally noisy, or one who is in need of quiet and privacy.

In this studio is a 100-foot mural painted in 1942 on canvas by a good friend of Béla's, Leo Katz. This painting, entitled "Metamorphosis," is an extraordinary work. As the artist himself says, it is a dream vision translated into a mural composition. Perhaps it would be best to let the artist describe it:

Symbolic objects. In the center Pegasus, the mythological flying horse of creative imagination, with wings clipped, stands exhibited on a platform or shelf, meagerly supported. A book of blank pages. Two airplanes. One on the ground, propeller spinning, looks with stupid curiosity at his mythological ancestor. The other one shark-faced, flies with satanic cruelty through the air. A highway through the desert leading over a pass into an unknown land beyond the distant mountains. A black wall.

On both sides are caryatid-like figures. The left figure is a woman, still half tree, planted in a rocky soil. The breasts and the face are living flesh, but the eyes are blind, polished stones. The hand turns into dead branches which like tentacles, threaten the horse.

The right figure shows three phases. Half of the thorax is alive. The right arm is tied behind the body. The other half and the head are still unfinished as if an invisible sculptor had tried to chisel this figure out of the virgin rock. There is much work to be done before the form can be considered human. The unfinished mask of the face has two little windows through which eyes in agony wait for deliverance. The lower part is armored and mechanized. The legs are resting on two automobiles. One points forward, one backward. Both have no place to go, since all horsepower and speed of mechanized action can lead nowhere in a mythological, spiritual and creative vacuum. The rocks show physiognomies, ready to materialize, ape-like, savage, cruel, sadistic, serene, etc.

This mural goes beyond the narcistic limitations of current surrealism. It contains a universal message from the subconscious. The meaning of this dream? Your guess is as good as mine.

The composition is a new experiment in tri-directional perspective. The caryatid-like figures and the bottom wall move in the plane of the wall. The landscape moves into the distance back of the wall plane. The platform with the horse and the rocks with the

automobiles create a 'front-plastic' illusion into the
space in front of the wall. A full demonstration of this
dimensional effect cannot be expected from this small reproduction where the essential relation to the surrounding walls is missing. The treatment of details, light and
color was dictated by the given conditions of the room.

The third house, separated from the others by a five-minute
walk, was made over from the old farmhouse on the property.
The interior is more modest but has a charm of its own. Looking towards the southeast one sees sloping hills and green val-
leys stretching beyond for miles. The windows on this side of
the house are truly picture windows. The house itself stands at
the top of a chasm which drops steeply into the branches of tall
trees and high bushes. It is left to grow wild for the delight of
birds and animals.

"This," Béla explains, "is for special guests, for those who are
in love with nature, or just simply in love, or for artists or authors,
who need a high percentage of peace and quiet." If a telephone
exists, it is one with a muted voice.

In March of every year, Béla and Cathy drive up to Garrison
almost every week end in their Ford convertible, to direct the
work going on to set the three dwellings in order, ready for
their summer guests. Cathy has an aunt, a very useful aunt
Alice, wife of the architect, Julian Levi. She often travels with
Béla and Cathy to Garrison at this time to help in the work,
for she is full of energy and ideas and practical ways of doing
things. If her husband comes too, he provides the heavy critical
note as the idle supervisor who uses up any excess energy in
filling up and puffing on his pipe.

Another occasional helper is Ilona, Béla's sister, who is much
in demand for her constant good nature and her delightful
sense of humor. Ilona has lived with Cathy's mother on Park
Avenue in New York City, looking after her since the death of
Albert Fries at eighty-eight in 1951.

There is a great deal of work during the spring week ends
bringing the houses back into shape. At times they find that
squirrels have gotten in and have died there. But all this work

is made up for by the pleasure of having guests through the summer, when the place fills with gaiety and laughter. The Schicks invite friends from all walks of life, well known and un-known, both Americans and Europeans, as well as men of med-icine from Asia. But not by any means all of Béla's own pro-fession, for he likes to converse with people engaged in other work. His well-known curiosity makes Béla a good listener as well as talker. It is not often that the Schicks themselves are driven to the quiet of the studio.

Over a glass of club soda, ginger ale, or French wine, ques-tions are often fired at Béla: "Why did you actually come to America?. . . Did you ever regret it? . . . What do you think of American democracy?" Until Dr. Schick is driven to cry out, "Please not everything at once! Let's make some order out of this. There's nothing unusual about it. It's simply a matter of. . . . Well, I've talked so much about this before, but that's nothing. I'll say it again. . . ."

He then settles himself comfortably in his chair and begins talking quietly, unhurriedly shifting his glass of ginger ale from hand to hand occasionally.

"After the end of the First World War, the resources that could be devoted to science on the other side of the ocean were extremely limited. On the other hand, it seems that, basically, the people of Europe are not as prone to new dis-coveries as elsewhere. When we tried to immunize them against diphtheria, they ran away from us—just as they did when Pasteur tried to use his treatment to prevent rabies.

"In America the situation is quite different. Most of the peo-ple here are very anxious and eager to try out any new ex-periment, possibly even too anxious. One of the things I do not enjoy particularly is to see a great deal of publicity given in the newspapers to a medical discovery before it is completely tested and perfected because I know for a certainty that I will be deluged the day after the discovery is announced with tele-phone calls and letters from people who would like to try this new remedy even before it has been proven and is ready to be given to the public.

"After the close of the First World War, I was firmly con-

vinced that there could be no foreseeable future and hope for
Europe . . . at least for the immediate future. Therefore, when I
was offered the position in a New York hospital, I was more than
happy to oblige and I came willingly, knowing quite well that
even though I was leaving my old home behind me, I was going
forward to a new and better home on the other side of the
water."

One of his more skeptical listeners voices an objection,
"When you arrived in the United States, there weren't too
many medical institutions. In the face of that weren't you afraid
to come here?"

"I already had a place to work for I was coming to assume
a position in a hospital," Béla explains patiently. "Naturally,
in the beginning, America was so engaged in constructing cities
and building industries that it couldn't have much time or energy to build institutions for medical research. It is entirely different now. We have some of the best medical schools and research laboratories in this country that can be found any place in
the world . . . and in addition we have countless numbers of
splendid doctors who were wholly trained in America. It is impossible for me to envision how we could fail to lead the rest
of the world in medical discoveries with a foundation such as
that.

"Health is dependent on many things. For example, we are
well aware of the fact that the latest remedies and scientific
discoveries and innovations are of little value, even the latest and
most advanced surgical methods are valueless without proper
health education, sanitation and other services, which, you know,
we have much better developed than anywhere else."

Béla sighs, drains the remaining contents of the glass, and
continues. "Now, I'll tell you as an ordinary human being, who
never had anything to do with politics—and I'll tell you as well
as I can—what I think of democracy. To me, democracy is a
certain way of life which, as an ordinary and integral part of its
very existence, concerns itself with the well-being and health
of the people. Only a peace-loving government, such as in a
democracy, could endeavor to develop high standards of living
for all of its people. On the other hand, contrastingly so, other

nations, whose ideologies are based on the thought and idea of conquest, are liable to force science into the service of their warlike aims and neglect all other phases of life for the populace.

"One can say that liberty and health are in some ways quite similar. People usually fail to cherish either of them, or even realize their merit and value, until they have been lost."

Béla pauses for emphasis, and leans forward a little in his chair. "If it were only possible for us to take precautions now to preserve our freedom, we might be able to avoid the disaster that could eventually threaten us. Unfortunately, at the present time, it seems to me, we are too certain that we are safe. We are too aware of our great resources and our higher standard of living. We are not conscious of the fact that we may be carrying the very germs of disease within our bodies. Why, even Plato recognized in his *Republic* that freedom would be endangered by the very forces which threaten it today."

Lounging in an armchair in Garrison talking and being talked at, Béla is quite happy. It is part of the joy of living on his own land. No longer do Béla and Cathy travel to Europe every summer, and the upkeep of the three houses means a great deal of work, despite the assistance they get from hired help. Still more does the upkeep of the grounds take up their time. But all these are the sacrifices they accept with a zestful eagerness.

There are many days in the early spring or the late fall when they sneak away from their friends in New York and drive up to Garrison in their green Ford, leaving on Friday and returning on the following Monday, tired, overworked, with scratched and bruised hands—the unmistakable signs that they have been working.

The Schicks invite their guests only when the place is in order. One has to be a very close friend indeed to be invited to Garrison to lend a hand in the preparations, in cleaning up the garden, or in painting the benches and wooden chairs which stand on the veranda on rainy days, and are placed on the grass by the swimming pool when the sun shines.

In addition to rest and relaxation and manual work about the garden, Béla is always taken up with care of the children's playthings, together with implements used in various methods of therapy for those children who are ill. His single aim is to make these children contented and happy. One of his latest inventions is a special bedpan for them.

Dr. Dan Holbrooke, as one of the frequent week-end guests up at Garrison, has described Béla wearing his khaki shorts, puttering about the garden, or cooking delicious meals for the fun of it, or relaxing in a chair while he launches into one of his many stories, which usually stem from his trips with Cathy.

Dan tells one story of his own about the Schick home in Garrison. Among his many occupations, he has become medical consultant to the Indian government. Thus he became acquainted with perhaps the greatest Indian physician, Dr. B. C. Roy, at present Prime Minister of West Bengal. Dr. Roy asked Dan to introduce him to Dr. Schick, and he came away very impressed. He described Béla to Dan as being just like an Indian "guru."

Dr. Roy was not satisfied with this one visit. He asked Dan to take him up to Garrison to meet with Béla Schick again. Béla received his guests with great joy, and the conversation that afternoon was lively. It turned eventually to the problem of educating Indian parents to the necessity of vaccination and elementary hygiene. Béla recounted his experiences in many countries where he was asked for advice, and he described how the respective local authorities handled the problem.

Both Dan and Cathy expressed surprise that Béla and Dr. Roy were talking on the subject as though it were impossible to use logic to convince the people.

"The only logical thing to do in those areas," said Béla at once, "is to avoid all use of logic. Most people don't know how to follow logic. They are so used to mystic thinking."

"Yes," agreed Dr. Roy, "as a doctor and as chief of a government, I can tell you that what people want is not logic, but magic."

"That is it in a nutshell," laughed Béla. "Magic not logic." Then someone spoke of the case in the African jungle when the administration of penicillin had to be accompanied by the beating of drums.

Dan Holbrooke concludes his story: "When Dr. Roy returned two years later, he again asked me to take him to Dr. Schick, and there in a small and cozy gathering, that man who had attained such prominence in India paid a personal tribute hard to equal. He had put Dr. Schick's photograph on his desk, Dr. Roy said, 'so that when I am sad and discouraged, I can look at that face, which is like a child's with a ray of sunshine in it.'"

CHAPTER TWENTY-FOUR

A Day of Work

SEVEN A.M. THE FRAGRANCE OF EARLY SPRING DRIFTED ALONG THE street from Central Park. In apartment number 1, 17 East 84th Street, there were sounds of activity. From the kitchen came the heartening smell of freshly brewed coffee. At least it was heartening to Béla Schick, who stood in his underwear in the middle of the bedroom, a sheaf of papers in his hand.

He called out, "It's good you're making breakfast already. But where are my trousers? I've been searching everywhere, and I cannot find them."

He looked down at the papers in his hand, and thought aloud to himself, "Now, how did these papers get into my hand at just this particular moment? I must have picked them up while I was looking for my clothes." He stared down at the papers. On top was a postcard. He could see the date, and it astonished him—January 7, 1931. He turned it over and read the message in large bold letters:

A Marked Improvement in Diphtheria Toxin for the Schick Test.

Under this was printed:

This is now offered by Parke, Davis & Co., in diluted form—ready for use:

Bio. 75 containing 10 Schick Tests

Bio. 78 containing 50 Schick Tests
Bio. 77 containing 100 Schick Tests
We can supply these promptly.

J. Leon Lascoff & Son
New York City, 1209 Lexington Avenue.

Béla stated loudly, "That's an old story. Those are ancient times." He began studying another piece of mail, still standing in the middle of the small bedroom.

In the meantime, Cathy left the kitchen and smiling gently came to the bedroom door.

Without looking up, Béla shouted a bit louder, "Cathy, where are my trousers?"

He was about to repeat the question a bit more impatiently, but was stopped by the fact that the garment in question had landed on top of his head. He extricated himself without a word, and started to put on the trousers. But he still held the pile of papers in his right hand. His eyes fell on the title of a medical reprint. He read: "'Fate and Effects of Injected Protein Antigens' by Charles A. Janeway, Harvard Medical School and Children's Medical Center, Boston."

Cathy, smiling to see her husband's second distraction, peered over his shoulder, and she read the dedication aloud: "To Dr. Schick, to whose beautiful work and keen insight the ultimate solution of the problem of allergy will ultimately be due." Then she read the date: "February 11, 1953."

Cathy moved round to face her husband. "Not bad," she said. "In fact very nice. Charles Janeway. Isn't that the Doctor Janeway who gave the annual Schick lecture in the Blumenthal Auditorium just three years ago?"

"Yes," said Béla, finally laying the papers on a nearby chair, and putting on his trousers. "An interesting person. Most intelligent." He glanced at his wife for the first time. She was going around the room picking things up off the floor. It was an effort to bring some sense of order back to the room. "How many lectures have there been so far, Cathy?"

"Count them yourself," she teased. "The first one was 1943, and now it is 1954."

Almost immediately after Dr. Schick's resignation from the

office of chief of the Pediatric Department, the Board of Trustees
and the medical staff of Mount Sinai Hospital organized what
they named the Béla Schick Lecture. Every year a renowned
specialist in certain branches of medicine is invited to deliver a
lecture. Each of these guest lecturers talks of his own work in
relation to the development of the problem from the work of
Schick pioneer days to the latest achievement in that particular
sphere. Naturally, these are highly specialized lectures interesting primarily men and women working in certain fields of medicine.

Among those who have given lectures are: Dr. A. Ashley
Weech, Professor of Pediatrics at the University of Cincinnati;
Dr. Arnold Gesell of Yale University; Michael Heidelberger,
Professor of Biochemistry at Columbia University; the 1952 No-
bel Prize winner in microbiology, Dr. Selman A. Waksman of
Rutgers University; L. Emmett Holt, Jr., Professor of Pediatrics
of New York University; and Dr. John F. Enders of the Boston
Children's Medical Center.

After each of these lectures, a reception is tendered for the
speaker, the audience, and Cathy and Béla. This usually
consists of a buffet supper at the home of one of Dr. Schick's
wealthy friends, or perhaps at the home of his mother-in-law,
Mrs. Albert Fries, who is most happy when she has many people around her.

This morning, Béla and Cathy drifted into reminiscing about
these lectures. Cathy was the first to spring back to alertness
with the smoke of burned food in her nostrils. She rushed into
the kitchen to find the coffee had boiled away, the eggs were
hard as rocks. Laughing at their own foolishness, they made
the best of a strange meal; hard boiled eggs on black bread and
freshly made orange juice. Ten minutes to eight! Béla, receiving
a kiss from his wife and a warning to be careful—for he was
going to be seventy-seven in three more months—departed ener-
getically to the street. He took in the beautiful April morning,
breathed the bracing air, gazed affectionately at four young
maples standing in front of his house with their newly formed
filigree of green leaves, and turned in the direction of Park

Avenue, briskly moving towards the Lexington Avenue subway at 86th Street.

Punctually at eight, he stepped into the Brooklyn express. It just happened that a young boy offered him a seat in the packed subway, but at 14th Street he gave up this seat to an elderly lady who muttered some indistinguishable remarks in Italian as a thank you.

8:30 A.M. He got off at Utica Avenue, Brooklyn, where he was supposed to be met by Dr. Alla Dunewitz, a close companion of Cathy's at the winter concerts and operas. But her car was not there. He walked to her house, saw the car in the street but no one in it. He entered her elegant apartment. Loud symphonic music greeted him, but no sign of Alla. He looked about for her, called her name. He went in to her doctor's study, just as she came into it from another entrance. They surprised each other, and laughingly extended their hands in greeting.

"Oh, I'm a bit late," she exclaimed. "Please forgive me. I was given some new records. Prokofieff. I just had to play them. I have to prepare myself, as you know, for a full day's work."

Béla laughed. "And because of your musical preparation, I have to be late at the hospital."

She turned off the music, and smiled at him. "Well, let's go." She took his arm.

In fifteen minutes they arrived at Beth-El Hospital, Linden Boulevard and Rockaway Parkway. In this hospital, which has 370 beds, Dr. Schick serves as the chief of the Pediatric Department, naturally, as always, without much compensation. His first stop inside the hospital was the room where ten premature infants were being cared for under the direction of the senior nurse, Helen Fine. A short discussion with her on the health of the babies, a check of the book, noting the health records of these small patients for the preceding night, and then a visit to their incubators for a personal check of their condition. Thus he finished the routine for that room.

He looked up at Helen, an energetic conscientious nurse. "Everything is in order. They're growing and are well."

She nodded at him brightly.

Then he began to laugh. "I cannot help but wonder why they didn't want to stay inside their mothers just a short while longer. They would have it better there, more comfortable and safer than in our world, this world built for them by adult maniacs."

Helen laughed, and shrugged her shoulders. "Yes," she said, "I've often wondered. Why do certain children want to be born before their time and others after their time?"

"Neither one nor the other should be necessary. And I imagine that some day someone will solve the riddle. But in the meantime we have to make sure they stay with us now they are here. You are their mother and you'll have to take care of them." With these words he smiled and left.

The next place he visited was the ward for new but normally born babies. There were about thirty. The resident assistant, Dr. Sonia Feldsher, was just checking them, or rather was just finishing her inspection, having been at work that day since seven in the morning. Dr. Schick sat himself down in a small room going over the health records of these children, making notes. Dr. Feldsher, a well and fully proportioned woman of great capabilities, came in. Dr. Schick greeted her and made some suggestions as to the treatment of the newborn. They were joined presently by Dr. Henry Galld, resident at the hospital, who had been making some interesting observations during the past year as a pediatrician. Postmature babies were his own specialty.

The three of them entered a ward with about thirty older children suffering varying ailments, from a five-year-old girl with a stubborn eczema which covered the entire body, to a boy of six and a half who was paralyzed in the right arm and leg and had lost his faculty for speech after an attack of so-called virus infection.

While Dr. Schick was examining these unfortunate children, a group of other doctors joined him in order to listen to the significant things he had to say. There was his old friend Dr. Mary Eleston; a young Italian from Sicily, Dr. Giuseppe D'Asquisto; Dr. Arturo Alvares from Colombia; two Americans from Brooklyn, Dr. Bernard Redner and Dr. Jerome Harris.

The latter was busy planning another pediatric ward for the hospital. Béla Schick was listened to with rapt attention, for here was their master speaking.

Before lunch, Dr. Schick hurried to the fifth floor of the hospital. He had various problems to discuss with young Dr. Peter Gruenwald, chief pathologist of the hospital, and one of the most capable in the country in Dr. Schick's estimation. The young man had already attracted attention with his interesting paper entitled, "Asphyxia, Trauma and Shock at Birth."

Their discussions always went deep into complex problems. This one began with talk of the two forms of allergy which Dr. Schick had explained in the anniversary article of the *Journal of the Mount Sinai Hospital,* one form of allergy being a physiologic one, the beneficial one making it possible to fight diseases due to the invasion of pathogenic microorganisms. This leads to immunity. As Béla Schick summarized it, foreign protein is fought with a similar defense mechanism, but the reaction to it is accompanied by a pathologic hypersensitivity. This, Dr. Schick pointed out, is frequently harmful, and may even be dangerous. Such a form of allergy he calls pathologic allergy, not to be confused with the normal, useful, physiologic allergy. Dr. Schick warned against stressing this negative form of allergy, for the beneficial and life-saving effects of the physiologic form outweigh by far the disadvantages of the other.

But the discussion shifted inevitably to the important problem now engaging Béla Schick, the question of the newborn; first the problem of allergy in the newborn; second, the matter of virus infection in the newborn; and then the questions: How do we prevent prematurity, and how do we prevent postmaturity?

It was hardly strange therefore that Dr. Schick should visit the laboratories, testing and experimenting himself, as well as searching for confirmation of his theories in the work of his younger colleagues, whom, as always, he had inspired and encouraged to concentrate on these problems which were his interest.

On the ground floor, in the hospital cafeteria, Dr. Schick stood in line with the other workers to select his lunch, a glass of tomato juice, two pieces of French toast with apple sauce, fruit salad, and instead of milk, the cup of coffee he had missed at breakfast. This free lunch could be considered his one form of payment for his work at Beth-El.

Dr. Schick finally left the hospital, hailed a taxi, and got out at the Utica Avenue subway station, to return to Manhattan by subway. There was need for haste as he was due to deliver a lecture on tuberculosis and the examination of complicated cases of this disease at 2:15 P.M. at the Willard Parker Hospital at the foot of East 15th Street.

He found twenty young doctors waiting to hear him and to ply him with their endless questions on consumptive tuberculosis. Béla spoke of it as a "discussion," and he continued talking for almost two hours. Although this should have been an exhausting task for even a young professor, he showed no sign of fatigue when he finished. He left with a feeling of superb elation. He had long ago discovered the thrill and creative meaning of teaching the younger generation.

From Willard Parker Hospital, he traveled uptown to Mount Sinai to devote several more hours to his work.

Everyone who meets him on these days is aware of a pending surprise that is likely to astound the entire medical profession, for from his manner of action, from what he says, and perhaps more precisely from what he does not say, it is clear to his colleagues that Béla Schick is about to come up with some answers on the great and puzzling problem of prematurity and postmaturity. Perhaps when Dr. Schick is through—provided one can ever speak of Dr. Schick as having concluded study on any problem—he will have made the most important set of discoveries of his entire career, and we shall find ourselves able to control the arrival of an infant into the world.

It was already eight o'clock when he left the hospital laboratory. He visited a flower shop on Madison Avenue, and bought a bouquet of violets for his Cathy. Then he hurried home.

Upon greeting his wife, Béla Schick found that his working day was not over—it seldom was at that early hour. He learned from Cathy that he was to be a guest at a reception to promote the building of a College of Medicine sponsored by Yeshiva University.

This medical school, now called the Albert Einstein College of Medicine, is to be part of the Bronx Municipal Hospital Center, built at a cost of $36,500,000 by the City of New York at Eastchester Road, Seminole Avenue and Pelham Parkway. The Pediatric Department will bear the name of Béla Schick.

It is a great honor, indeed, but for Dr. Schick it means also one more added responsibility.

During the reception one of the younger physicians, too shy to question the master in public, came over to Béla and asked quietly, "Dr. Schick, what is your definition of a genius, please?"

For the moment Béla was taken aback, then he replied solemnly, "Ninety per cent hard and prolonged labor until your sweat soaks your body, plus ten per cent of luck."

Thus the portrait of a twentieth century's medical genius, Béla Schick.

As I come to the end of this narrative, news reached me that Dr. Schick was to have still further recognition of his contributions to medical science. On May 3rd, 1954, at its annual meeting, The American Pediatric Society awarded the coveted John Howland Medal to Béla Schick.

Epilogue

BY DR. EDWARDS A. PARK

Professor Emeritus of Pediatrics, Johns Hopkins University

IT IS A PLEASURE TO READ ABOUT MY GREAT FRIEND, BÉLA SCHICK, whom I so wholly admire, and, when self-seeking, bigoted, evil men keep our minds in turmoil and make us anxious and fearful for the future, it should be a relief to you to be led away for a little into the green pastures and still waters of his tranquil life, so masterfully described by Antoni Gronowicz.

He was born prematurely at the home of his granduncle, Dr. Telegdy, where his mother happened to be visiting. It is said that his mother inquired of her uncle, at the time of his birth, if the baby was worth saving, a question which indicated great mental detachment. The remarkableness of the question and its unusualness under the circumstances make one wonder if Schick did not owe to his mother in large part at least his highly original intellectual inheritance. The photograph of the mother shows a lovely-looking young woman with a mouth suggesting great force. The face is not exactly beautiful, but far better than that, the face of a woman one would love to have known, and knowing, would have liked.

As a premature infant Schick has a distinguished competitor. Sir Isaac Newton was a premature infant and his mother in after years used to boast that she could have put him in a quart jug. We are all curious to know how much the infant, Béla, weighed, and whether Mrs. Schick, in her turn, could have fitted him into a liter stein.

He was brought up and attended school in Graz and then took his medical degree at the Karl Franz University in that town. It was in Graz that Schick started work under Escherich. He worked in the Escherich clinic in Vienna as a voluntary assistant for a year and a half without compensation, supporting himself by doing odd jobs. But he had charge of the Scarlet Fever Pavilion and it was there and then that his knowledge of scarlet fever began which later made him a world authority. He arrived in Vienna in 1902 and soon after joined von Pirquet, another pupil of Escherich, in the studies on immunity.

Schick has described in a letter, written me some years ago, his relations with von Pirquet at this early period.

> Pirquet started his scientific pediatric work with Dr. Moser, first assistant at the Escherich Clinic. They proved the specificity of streptococci found in the heart blood culture of scarlet fever patients by means of agglutination. We used Moser's scarlet fever serum and had the opportunity of studying the vaccine reaction. Large amounts of sera (180 cc.) had to be used. The result was excellent. I was working with Pirquet who was resident, I the intern or volunteer. Thus I became close to his work.
>
> Pirquet took me as his collaborator. Studying together the serum disease I found the accelerated reactions due to accelerated reproduction of antibodies after those from the final injection had been destroyed. We extended his studies to other diseases, particularly to vaccination, and to the tuberculin reaction which Pirquet at first did not consider an allergic reaction. . . . The book on serum disease and study of vaccination was meanwhile published.

Pirquet and Schick worked together on their common problem from 1902 until 1909. No one knows the intellectual relationship of the two men and I doubt if they knew themselves. I have always suspected that their minds in some remarkable way complemented each other. They were totally different. After a most painstaking clinical study of measles von Pirquet wandered off into the fields of nutrition and public health and his interest turned more and more to public health and administration. He had great administrative ability and became a powerful commanding figure in Austrian postwar politics. If circumstances had turned out slightly differently, he might well have left medicine altogether for a political career. Certainly von Pirquet's greatest achievements were when he was working in close association with Schick. Schick, in contrast to von Pirquet, led always an academic, almost cloistered life, remained completely engrossed in clinic medicine and its problems and never extended or had any desire to extend beyond them.

Although it is impossible to analyze the "marriage of true minds" which existed between them, the importance of their combined contributions to medical science is clear enough. In my opinion at least, their studies of immunity represent the finest contributions to medicine ever made by pediatricians. They perceived and defined the general principles of immunity, as developed in their investigations of serum sickness, then of vaccination against smallpox and finally tuberculosis. I do happen to know that Schick was the one to perceive the nature of the accelerated reaction in immunity, a conception difficult to grasp and of obvious basic importance. I doubt if knowledge in this field has advanced much further, except in details, than von Pirquet and Schick left it and it will never make great further progress until it is possible to understand the chemical nature of the factors involved in immune reactions, and to substitute in our thinking chemical reactions for the unknown quantities of algebra. How Escherich's heart must have glowed with pride when he saw these two boys, for they were scarcely more than that, penetrate step by step into this *terra incognita* and return, laden with its rich spoils. When Schick began work with von Pirquet he was but twenty-six and von Pirquet only three years older.

Von Pirquet's and Schick's studies of the principles of immunity led to the practical discoveries of the von Pirquet test for tuberculosis and the Schick test for immunity to diphtheria.

As Schick has written, he was the one to perceive the allergic nature of the tuberculin test but his attention centered on the subcutaneous reaction; it was von Pirquet's great merit to apply the test to the skin. In 1906 Schick transferred from the Scarlet Fever to the Diphtheria Pavilion and his special interest in diphtheria is explained in that way.

It is actually unnecessary to discuss the importance of the Schick test for immunity in diphtheria. I might remark in passing, however, that it was the third step of the series which has resulted in the suppression of diphtheria. The first was the discovery by Klebs and Löffler of the bacillus. This discovery made it possible to identify the disease and to learn its prevalence and distribution in the community. The second was the discovery by von Behring of diphtheria antitoxin, which rendered cure possible. The next was Schick's discovery which made it possible to check not only the susceptibility of the individual but of the community. The final step was the development of methods for depriving the toxin of injurious properties while retaining its antigenic power, an accomplishment which came about gradually as the result of work by several different investigators. As an illustration of the importance of Schick's discovery, if we were able to detect those susceptible to infantile paralysis and at the same time had the means of immunizing them, the disease could be made, practically speaking, to cease.

One of Schick's additional remarkable contributions to medicine was his monograph on scarlet fever, a work which is a classic today.

The First World War came in 1914, and during that period until its close in 1918, Schick worked on the Newborn Service. It was about this time that he reported toxic manifestations during menstruation. This observation far away from the field of his immediate interest illustrates one of his remarkably developed powers.

In 1923 Schick came to the United States to assume his duties at Mount Sinai Hospital in New York City. I shall not discuss his career and activities in Mount Sinai because you are all familiar with them after the reading of this biography.

In 1925 Schick lowered his banner as a confirmed bachelor

and surrendered to Catharine Fries. My friend, Dr. Kohn, writes, "I always tell him that this was his most valuable discovery." I might suggest to Dr. Kohn that this was also his easiest, one for which he does not deserve any particular credit.

I should now like to say something about Dr. Schick's personal qualities, as they appear to me to be, although I am conscious that my remarks may be embarrassing. It is dreadful to be analyzed, particularly in public. Even though the things said are good, the victim squirms, but perhaps they will be pleasant in retrospect.

Interests are natural to him and, one becoming established, he follows it with an absorbing intensity and perseverance to some kind of conclusion. The result is that he concentrates all his force on any problem which he undertakes. His mind is the kind which demands the reason for things and is extraordinarily fertile and imaginative in ideas. Then, in addition, there is something there which requires that ideas be put to the practical test. This impulse or habit of continually testing his imagination is one of the secrets of his success. So many of us never go to the trouble to plant our ideas in order to see if they are capable of growth.

His thinking is fresh, quite independent of currents or fashions of thought and therefore without bias, often diverging from accepted thought or actually running opposite to it. His thinking is *sui generis* arising from a completely clean surface as if no other thinking existed. Originality of mind is merely the ability to think differently correctly. In his investigations his thinking seems very simple and the means which he employs have been simple. He does not use intricate methods. The tools on which he relies are his powers of observation and his thoughtfulness. His success illustrates that many of nature's secrets are close to the surface and visible to those having the wit to see them. He is every inch a scholar. He has not lived, almost literally, night and day for years in contact with sick children, without having stored away a wealth of experience, the kind transferred directly via the eyes, ears and hands, not secondhand, not forgotten, not found in books.

The reason that he is a great teacher is because his store of knowledge is so great and so unique. I believe that he shines most as a teacher of the privileged few because the gems of experience fall as the result of the jostlings of chance rather than by intention and one has to be close in order to pick them up.

In character he is so simple, open and friendly, so shy as almost to be called bashful, and so good and kind that to become acquainted with him is to love him. I once asked Dr. Stone, the well known surgeon of the Children's Hospital, about Dr. James Jackson Putnam, the well known neurologist and psychiatrist. I have always remembered Dr. Stone's answer: "Goodness and kindness oozed out of him at every pore and stuck to him, too, like 'lasses to a kid's face.'" We could say the same of Schick so excellently portrayed in this highly absorbing book.

WORKS OF DR. BÉLA SCHICK

Hypertrophia Cerebri. *Jahrb. f. Kinderh.* 57: 423, 1903.

Variabilitaet der Diphtheriebacillen. *Wr. klin. W.* 16: 993, 1903.
With H. Ersettig

Zur Theorie der Inkubationszeit. *W. klin. W.* 16: 758, 1903.
With v. Pirquet

Zur Theorie der Vakzination. *Vehr. Ges. Kind.,* 1903
With v. Pirquet

Urotropin und Scharlachnepthritis. *Wr. klin. ther. W.* 17: 967, 1904.

Spezifische Agglutination von Streptokokken aus Scharlachanginen, etc. *Wr. klin. W.* 18: 3, 1905.
With E. Rossival

Weitere Erfolge der Serumbehandlung des Scharlachs. *D. med. W.* 31: 2092, 1905.

Die Diagnostische Tuberkulinreaktion in Kindesalter. *Jahrb. Kinderh.* 61: 811, 1905.

Serumkrankheit. Monographie. Verl. Deuticke, Wien, 1905.
With v. Pirquet

Zur Frage des Agressins. *Wr. klin. W.* 18: 431, 1905.
With v. Pirquet

Postscarlationose Lymphadenitis. *Jahrb. Kinderh.* 62: 661, 1906.

Nachkrankheiten, Infektiositaet and Therapie des Scharlachs. *Handb. Kinderh.* Pfaundler-Schlossman. I. Aufl. Verlag Vogel, Leipzig, 1906.

Serumkrankheit. *Handb. Kinderh.* Pfaundler-Schlossman. I. Aufl. Verlag Vogel, Leipzig, 1906.
With v. Pirquet

Ueberempfindlichkeit und beschleunigte Reaktion. *Muench. m. W.* 103: 66, 1906.
With v. Pirquet

Nachkrankheiten des Scharlachs. *Jahrb. Kinderh.* 65: 132, 1907.
Therapie des Scharlachs. *Berl. klin. W.* 44: 709, 1907.
Herzstoerungen bei Scharlach. Verh. D. Ges. Kinderh. 1907.
Chlorstoffwechsel und Koerpergewicht im Scharlach. *Zeitsch. klin. Med.* 66: 352, 1908.
With O. Gruener
Ueber ein den Koplikschen Flecken analoges Frühsymptom der Masern an der Caruncula. *Mit. Ges. Innern Med. u Kind.,* Wien 7: 64, 1908.
Kutanreaktion bei Impfung mit Diphtherietoxin. *Muench. Med. W.* 55: 504, 1908.
Diphtheriekutanreaktion. *Verh. Deutsch. Ges. Kinderh.* 25: 330, 1908.
Die Physiologische Nagellinie des Saeuglings. *Jahrb. Kinderh.* 67: 137, 1908.
Sulla Cutireazione Difterica. *Biochimica e Terapia Sperimentale* 1: 1, Milano 1909.
Intrakutane Wertbestimmung des Diphtherieantitoxins. *Handb. Technik und Methodik* der Imm. Forsch., Kraus-Levaditi, 1909.
Diphtheriekutanreaktion beim Meerschweinchen. *Zeitsch. Immun.* 4: 550, 1909.
With E. Novotny
Homologe und Heterologe Passive Anaphylaxie. *Zeitsch. Immun.* 3: 671, 1909.
With E. Novotny
Ueber ein durch Trauma Ausloesbares Postscarlatinoeses Exanthem (Erythema Postscarlatinosum) Jahrbuch f. Kinderheilkunde 71: 123 1910.
Gehalt des Serums Di-und Masernkranker Kinder an Schutzkoerper gg. Di-Toxin. *Jahrb. Kind.* 72: 460, 1910.
With M. Karasawa
Untersuch. u. d. Gehalt Menschlicher Sera an Schutzkoerper gg. Di-toxin. *Jahrb. Kind.* 72: 144, 1910.
With M. Karasawa
Quantitative Bestimmung des Resorptionsverlaufes Subcutan eingef. Di-serums. *Zeitsch. Kind.* 1: 62, 1910.
With M. Karasawa

Vakzineinfektion des Kaninchens m. Intrakutaner Injektion v. Kuhpockenlymphe. *Zeitsch. Immun.* 5: 688, 1910.
With E. Novotny

Scharlach. *Handb. Kinderh.* Pfaundler-Schlossman. 2 Aufl. Leipzig, Vogel, 1910.

Scheinbares Aufflammen abg. Tuberkulinreaktionen waehrend der Eruption von Masern. *Monatsschr. f. Kinderh.* 5: 137, 1910.

Exspiratorisches Keuchen als Symptom der Lungendruesentbc. im I. Lebensjahre. *Wien. klin. Wo.* 23: 135, 1910.

Roeteln. *Erg. Inn. Med. Kinderh.* Verlag Springer, Berlin 5: 280, 1910.

Diphtherie-Immunitaet. *Verh. Deutsche Ges. Kindh.* 28: 212, 1911.
With M. Karasawa

Passive Uebertragung der Intrakutanen Tuberculinreaktion beim Meerschweinchen. *Zeitsch. f. Immun.* 9: 275, 1911.
With E. Novotny

Versuche mit intrakutaner Injektion von Diphtherietoxin. Deutsche Ges. F. Kinderh., Muenster, 1912.
With Fr. Magyar

Diphtheriekutanreaktion beim Meerschweinchen bei wiederholter Injektion. *Zentralbl. f. Bakt.* 66: 121, 1912.
With So

Wertbestimmung des Schutzkoerpergeh. Menschl. Serums durch Intrakutane Inj. beim Menschen. *Zeitschr. f. Kindh.* 5: 349, 1912.

Behandlung des Scharlachs mit Moserserum. *Therapeut. Monatsh.* 26: 258, 1912.

Intrakutanreaktion d. Menschen auf Di-toxininjektion als Ausdruck d. Schutzkoerpergehaltes seines Serums. *Zeitschr. f. Kindh.* 5: 232, 1912.
With Michiels

Zwei Faelle von Familiaerer Spin. Muskelatrophie. *Wiener Med. Wo.* 62: 1186, 1912.

Scharlach. Monographie. Nothnagel Handbuch. Verlag Hoelder, Wien, 1912.
With Th. Escherich

Malignes Granulom mit Recurrierendem Fieber. *Zeitschr. f. Kindh.* 5: 493, 1913.

Diphtheriehautreaktion als Vorprobe d. Prophylakt. Diphtherieseruminjektion. *Muench. M. Wo.* 60: 2608, 1913.

Spezifische Therapie der Diphtherie Referat Mikrobiologentag. *Zentralbl. f. Bakt. Beiheft* 57: 16, 1913.

Experimentelle Diphtherieserumtherapie. *Gesellsch. F. Kindh.* 30: 168, 1914.
With Busacchi u. Kassowitz

Experimentelle Diphtherieserumtherapie. *Zeitschr. f. exp. Med.* 4: 83, 1914.
With Busacchi u. Kassowitz

Verhalten d. Menschen geg. Ausgeglichenen Toxin-Antitoxin Misch. *Zeitschr. f. exp. Med.* 4: 305, 1914.
With Kassowitz

Fortschritte in der Therapie der Diphtherie. *Wien. med. Wo.* 64: 1965, 1914.

Zur Frage der Physiol. Koerpergewichtsabnahme des Neugeborenen. *Zeitschr. f. Kindh.* 13: 257, 1915.

Der Kampf gegen die Tuberkulose des Kindesalters. *Oesterr. Sanitaetswesen* 27: 15, 1915.

Ein Fall von Beschneidungstbc. *Wien. klin. Wo.* 30: 1629, 1917.

Ernaehrungsstudien beim Neugeborenen I. Mitteilung. *Zeitschr. f. Kindh.* 17: 1, 1918.

Tuberkulose im Kindesalter. Klinik Prognose u. Behandlung. *Oesterr. Sanitaetswesen* 30: 334, 1918.

Das Pirquetsche System der Ernaehrung (auch als Broschuere in 2 Auflagen). *Erg. Inneren Med. u. Kindh.* 16: 384, 1919.

Ernaehrungsstudien beim Neugeborenen, 2. Mitt. *Zeitschr. f. Kindh.* 22: 195, 1919.

Nahrungsbedarf der Stillenden Frau. *Wien. M. Wo.* 69: 1557, 1919.

Nahrungsbedarf der Stillenden Frau. *Zeitschr. f. Kindh.* 21: 284, 1919.

Nahrungsbedarf der Frau im Letzten Drittel der Schwangerschaft. *Zeitschr. f. Kindh.* 23: 26, 1919.

Ernaehrungsstudien beim Neugeborenen 3. Mitt. *Zeitschr. f. Kindh.* 27: 57, 1920.

Freiluftspital f. Tuberkuloese Kinder. *Zeitschr. f. Kinderschutz* 12: 53, 1920.

Das Menstruationsgift (Menotoxin). *Wien Kl. Wo.* 33: 395, 1920.

Icterus Neonatorum sene Folge des Abbaues mütterlichen Blutes. *Zeitschr. f. Kindh.* 27: 231, 1920.

Das Pirquet'sche System und Seine Gegner. *Zeitschr. f. Kindh.* 28: 62, 1921.

Ueber Konzentrierte Ernaehrung und deren Indikation besonders im Sglsalter. I. Mitt. *Zeitschr. f. Kindh.* 30: 121, 1921.
With E. Helmreich

Ueber Konzentrierte Ernaehrung. 2 Mitt. Einfluss Wechselnder Konzentr. auf Koerpergew. u. Harnm. *Zeitschr. f. Kindh.* 30: 147, 1921.
With E. Helmreich

Ernaehrungsstudien beim Neugeborenen. 4. Mitt. *Zeitschr. f. Kindh.* 30: 363, 1921.
With E. Helmreich

Ueber eine Verdauungsstoerung jenseits des Saeuglingsalter, 1. Mitt. *Zeitschr. f. Kinderh.* 30: 223, 1921.
With R. Wagner

Neue Wege der Di-prophylaxe. *Llin Wo.* 1: 25, 1922.
With Kassowitz

Diphtheriediagnose. *Wien. med. Wo.* 72: 1484, 1922.

Ueber die Ursache des Negativen Ausfalles der Di-hautreaktion bei Maligner Di. *Klin. Wo.* 1: 1691, 1922.

Verdauungsstoerung jenseits des Saeuglingsalter. 2. Mitt. *Zeitschr. f. Kinderh.* 35: 263, 1923.
With R. Wagner

Intrakutane Reaktionen. *Handb. d. Biologischen Arbeitsmeth.* v. Abderhalden. Abt. XIII, Teil 2, pp. 507, 1923.
With von Groer and Kassowitz

Acetonstudien beim Neugeborenen. *Zeitschr. f. Kinderh.* 37: 363, 1924.
With R. Wagner

Verdeilung der Gelbfaerbung der Haut beim Icterus Neonatorum. *Zeitschr. f. Kinderh.* 38: 513, 1924.

Reorganisation of Nutrition Work to Save Food Waste in Childrens' Departments. *Modern Hospital* 23: 117, 1924.

The Development of the Intracutaneous Di-toxintest. *New York State J. M.* 24: 756, 1924.

Die Pulszahlen des Foetus, des Saeuglings und d. Kleinkindes. *Zeitschr. f. Kinderh.* 38: 216, 1924.

Observation of the Nutritional Effect of Subcutaneous Oil Injections. *Proc. Soc. Exp. Biol. & Med.* 21: 445, 1924.
With M. Fries, et al.

Concentrated Feeding. *Arch. Pediat.* 42: 397, 1925.

Health Conservation Class. *Hosp. Soc. Serv.* 12: 81, 1925.

Lowered Basal Metabolism in Postinfectious Stages and in Diseases Characterized by Slow Pulse Rate. *Am. J. Dis. Child.* 30: 291, 1925.
With Ph. Cohn

The Predisposing Factor in Diphtheria. *New York State M. J.* 114: 197,

The Basal Metabolism after Pneumonia. *Am. J. Dis Child.* 31: 228, 1926.
With A. Topper

Die Diphtherie-Intrakutan-Reaktion. *Wien Med. Wo.* 77: 755, 1927.

Tuberculosis in Childhood. *Med. Clin. North America* 12: 561, 1928.

Effect of Tonsillectomy and of Adenoidectomy on Di-immunity. *Am. J. Dis. Child.* 38: 929, 1929.
With A. Topper

Di-Schutzimpfung in den Ver. Staaten v. Nordamerica. *Erg. d. Sozialen Hyg. & Gesundh.* pflege Verl. Thieme, **Leipsig,** 1: 146, 1929.

Kindertuberkulose in Amerika. *Handb. d. Kindertuberkulose* Engel & Pirquet Verl. Thieme, Leipzig, 2: 1537, 1930.

Gefahrenzone bei der Aktiven Immunisierung gegen Diphtherie. *Wien. Med. Wo.* 80:   , 1930.

Behandlung der Serumkrankheit. *Kind. aerztl.* Praxis 1: 12, 1930.

Parenteral BCG Vaccine. *Am. J. Dis. Child* 43: 273-283, Feb., 1932.
With W. H. Park and C. Kereszturi

Clinical Observation in Parenteral BCG Vaccination. *Acta Paediat.* 2: 400, 1932.
With W.H. Park and C. Kereszturi
Zur Behandlung der Toxicose im Saeuglingsalter. *Zeitschr. f. Kinderh.* 53: 466, 1932.
Treatment of Alimentary Toxicosis. *J.A.M.A.* 99: 366-368, July 30, 1932; *Tr. Sec. Ped.*, A.M.A. pp. 66-73, 1932.
With S. Karelitz
Pathogenesis of Diphtheria. *Emanuel Libman Anniversary* 3: 1047, 1932. International Press.
Aktive Immunisierung gg. Diphtherie Referat Deutsche Ges. f. Kinderheilkunde Dresden. *Monatsschrift. f. Kinderh.* 51: 454, 1932.
Masernschutzimpfung mit Erwachsenenserum Reaktiviert durch Exposition zu Masern. *Wien. Med. Wo.* 82: 1395, 1932.
With S. Karelitz
Tubercle Bacilli in the Stomach Content of Children with Positive Tuberculin Test *J.A.M.A.* 98: 1879, 1932.
With C. Kereszturi, L. Mishulow, et al
Acid-fast Bacilli in the Stomach Lavage and Faeces of Tuberculous Children. *J.A.M.A.* 100: 1481, 1933.
With C. Kereszturi, D. Happtman, et al
Chemical Allergy and Nirvanol Sickness. *Am. J. Dis. Child.* 45: 1216, 1933.
With S. Peck and H. Sobotka
Metabolismo Basal en Los Ninos. *Paidoterapia,* June, 1933.
With A. Topper
Allergy. Roundtable Conference *I. J. Pediat.* 4: 75, 1934.
Child Care Today. (Textbook). Greenberg, N.Y. 1934.
With W. Rosenson
Abnormal Nutritional States in Children. *Med. Clin. North America* 17: 1219, 1934.
With A. Topper
Diphtherie. *Handb. d. Kinderh. Pfaundler-Schlossman.* 4. Auflage. 2: 1, 1934.
Allergy. Roundtable Conference II. *J. Pediat.* 5: 698, 1934.
Epidemiologic Factors in Measles Prophylaxis. *J.A.M.A.* 104: 991-994, March 23, 1935.

With S. Karelitz

Tuberculosis. Roundtable Conference. *J. Pediat.* 7: 855, 1935.

Congenital Malaria. *Mt. Sinai Hosp. Bull.* 2: 147, 1935.

With M. Stein

Follow-Up Study of 629 Tuberculous Children. *Seaview Hosp. Bull.* 1: 314, 1936.

With C. Kereszturi and H. Rosenberg

Die Infektionsgefahr in Kinderspitälern. *Wien. med. Wchnschr.* 86: 803-804, July 18, 1936.

Essential Xanthomatosis; Treatment with Cholesterol-Free Diet in 2 Cases. *Am. J. Dis. Child.* 51: 1372-1384, June, 1936.

With W.M. Sperry

Tuberculosis in Childhood. *M. Clin. North America* 20: 719-735, November, 1936.

Allergy and Immunity. *Radiol. Rev. & Mississippi Valley M.* 59: 1-7, January, 1937.

Pirquet Cubicles for Infants. *J.A.M.A.* 108: 1684-1688, May 15, 1937.

With S. Karelitz

Tuberculosis in Childhood. *Radiol. Rev. & Mississippi Valley Med. J.* 59: 177-182, September, 1937.

Zur Behandlung des Akuten Gelenk-Rheumatismus in Kindesalter. *Schweiz. med. Wchnschr.* 67: 987-988, October 9, 1937.

Typical Form of Splenomegaly in Childhood. Phlebosclerosis of portal circulation. *J. Mt. Sinai Hosp.* 4: 221-224, Nov.-Dec., 1937.

With M. Freund

Influence of Vitamin C on Diphtheria Toxin. *Am. J. Dis. Child.* 55: 12-26, January, 1938.

With J. Pakter

Skin Reaction with Diphtheria Toxin on Human Beings as Test Preceding Prophylactic Injection of Diphtheria Serum. *J. Mt. Sinai Hosp.* 5: 26-28, May-June, 1938 (Translated reprint).

Common Forms of Childhood Tuberculosis. *M. Clin. North America* 23: 645-660, May, 1939.

Child Care Today. Greenberg, New York. 1940

With W. Rosenson

Thoracoplasty in Children. *J. Mt. Sinai Hosp.* 7: 486-489, Jan.-Feb. 1941.
With B. Singer

Prevention of Dental Caries by Massive Doses of Vitamin D. *Am. J. Dis. Child.* 62: 1183-1187, December, 1941.
With R. H. Brodsky and H. Vollmer

Diphtheria in Litchfield and Dumbo. *Therapeutics in Infancy and Childhood.* F.A. Davis Co. Philadelphia. 1942.

Problem of Allergy in Rheumatic Disease. *J. Mt. Sinai Hosp.* 8: 991-994, Jan.-Feb., 1942.

Icterus Index of Cord Blood; Genesis of Icterus Neonatorum. *Am. J. Dis. Child.* 64: 655-660, October, 1942.
With S. B. Weiner and M. Reiner

Tea Prepared from Needles of Pine Trees Against Scurvy. *Science* 98: 241-242, Sept., 10, 1943.

Case of Neurofibromatosis in Child 5-3/4 years of age. *J. Mt. Sinai Hosp.* 10: 399-401, Sept.-Oct., 1943.

Edema with Hypoproteinemia due to Congenital Defect in Protein Formation (case report), *J. Pediat.* 27: 241-245, Sept., 1945.
With J.W. Greenbaum

Tratamiento de las Enfermedades Infeccionsas; Agentes Terapéuticos y Biológicos para Combatirlas; informe del Comité de la "American Academy of Pediatrics." *Arch. argent. de pediat.* 24: 228, September; 317, October, 1945.
With J. A. Toomey

Allergy and Immunity. *J. Mt. Sinai Hosp.* 14: 595. 1947.

The Newborn Service in New York. *Oesterreichische Zeitsch. fuer Kinderheilkunde und Kinderfuersorge,* Vienna, 3: 147, 1949.

Diaplacental Infection of the Fetus with the Virus of German Measles Despite Immunity of the Mother. Analogous Observations in Smallpox. *Acta Pediatrica,* 38: 563-570. 1949.

Placental Transmission of Mumps and Streptococcus M.G. Antibodies. *Proc. of Soc. for Experimental Biology and Medicine.* 78: 126-128, 1951.
With A. Florman and H. Scalattar

Physiologic and Pathologic Allergy. J. *of the Mt. Sinai Hosp.* 19: 240-242, 1952.
Five Articles. *Brennemann's Practice of Pediatrics*, 1948-1953:
1. Diphtheria. 2: Chapter 4.
2. Serum Sickness. 2: Chapter 2.
3. Immunity, Allergy and Anaphylaxis. 1: Chapter 4.
4. Bronchial Asthma. 2: Chapter 57.
5. Hayfever. 2: Chapter 58.
With M. Peshkin

SELECTED BIBLIOGRAPHY

Abramson, H.A., *Psychodynamics and the Allergic Patient,* Bruce Publishing Co., St. Paul, Minn., 1948.

Abt, Isaac A., The Influence of Pathology on the Development of Pediatrics, *Am. J. Dis. Child.,* xxxiv, 1, 1927.

Adams, Samuel S., The Evolution of Pediatric Literature in the United States, *Transactions of the American Pediatric Society,* New York, ix, 5, 1897.

Anderson, J.S., The Trend of Diphtheria, *Pub. Health,* London, 45: 98-202, 1931-32.

Arancio, V., La Lotta contro la Difteria; dal Siero di Behring alla Anatossina di Ramon, *Med. nuova,* 21: 283-91, 1930.

Armstrong, George, *An Account of the Diseases Most Incident to Children from their Birth till the Age of Puberty, with a Successful method of Treating them, etc.,* London, 1777.

Audouard, G., La diphtérie en Pays Rhénan, *Bull. et mém. Soc. med. d. hôp. de Par.,* 3. s., xlvi, 370-376, 1922.

Baginsky, A., Zur Serumbehandlung der Diphtherie, *Berl. Kl. Wo.* Nr. 52, 1894.

Baginsky, Adolph, *Handbuch der Schulhygiene,* F. Enke Stuttgart, 1900.

Baginsky und Katz, Die Erste Serie der mit Antitoxin (Aronson) Behandelten Diphtheriefälle, *Archiv. f. Kinderh.,* 18. Bd., p. 321.

Bail, Überempfindlichkeit bei Tuberculösen Thieren, *Wr. Klin. Wo.,* Nr. 30, 1904.

Baker, J., Allergy in Children as related to altitude. *Ann. Allergy,* 6:33, 1948.

Ballantyne, John Wm., *The Diseases and Deformities of the Foetus—and Thought Toward a System of Antenatal Pathology,* Edinburgh, 1895.

Bausfield, G.W.J., Diphtheria: the Present Position, *Practitioner,* London, 121: 237-44, 1932.

Beclère, Chambon and Ménard, Étude Expérimentale des Accidents Postserotherapiques, *Annales de l'Inst. Pasteur,* 1896.

Behring, Emil Adolph von, *Die Praktischen Ziele der Blutserumtherapie und die Immunisirungsmethoden zum Zweck der Gewinnung von Heilserum,* Leipzig, 1892.

Behring, Leistungen und Ziele in der Serumtherapie, *D. Med. Wo.* Nr. 38, 1895.

v. Behring und Kitashima, Über Verminderung und Steigerung der Ererbten Giftempfindlichkeit, *Berl. Klin. Wo.,* Nr. 6, p. 157, 1901.

Bernton, H.D., Asthma Due to a Mold-Aspergillus Fumigatus, *J.A.M.A.,* 95: 189, 1930.

Biedert, Philip, Neue Untersuchungen und Klinische Beobachtungen über Menschen und Kuhmilch als Kindernährungsmittel, *Virchow's Arch. f. path. Anat.,* ix, 352, 1874.

Biondo, A., On the Diagnostic and Prognostic Value of Takata-Ara's Reaction in the Blood Serum of Patients Suffering from Hepatic Affections, *Policlinico (Sez. Prat.),* 41: 1681, 1934.

Bokay, J., Die Diphtherie seit Bretonneau, *Erg. inn. Med. Kinderh.,* 42: 463; 42: 428, 1932.

v. Bokay, Die Heilserumbehandlung gegen Diphtherie im Budapester Stefanie-Kinderspital, *H. f. Kdh.,* 44, Bd., 1897.

Bolton, Ch., The Complications of the Serum Treatment of Diphtheria, *Lancet,* April, 1899.

Boucher, Extraordinaire Gravité de la Diphtérie Depuis les Inoculations de Behring et de Roux, *Trav. prat. d'obst. et de gynéc.,* Paris, 115-118, 1907.

Bretonneau; Pierre, *Des Infammations Speciales du Tissu muquex et en Particulier de la Diphtérite, Connue sous le Nom de Croup,* Paris, 1826.

Brown, G.T., Sensitization to Fungi, *Ann. Int. Med.* 6: 655, 1932. Hypersensitiveness to Fungi, *J. Allergy,* 7:455, 1936.

Brüning, Hermann, *Geschichte der Methodik der Künstlichen Säuglingsernährung,* F. Enke. Stuttgart, 1908.

Brüning und Schwalbe, *Handbuch der Allgemeinen Pathologie*

und der Pathologischen Anatomie des Kinderalters, J.F. Bergmann Wiesbaden, 1912.

Budin, Pierre, *Le Norrison,* 1900; English Translation, *The Nursling, The Feeding and Hygiene of Premature and Full-term Infants,* translated by Wm. J. Maloney, The Caxton Co., London, 1907.

Bujwid, O., Kann das Antidiphtherieserum schädlich sein? *Polnisch. ref. Virchow's Jahrb.,* II, p. 659, 1897.

Bukantz, S.C., Dammin, C.J., Wilson, K.C., Johnson, M.C., and H. L. Alexander, Inhibitory Effect of Nitrogen Mustard (bis-beta-chloroethyl-amine) on Lesions of Experimental Serum Hypersensitiveness, *Proc. Soc. Exp. Biol. Med.,* 72:21, 1949.

Cairns, On the Treatment of Diphtheria by the Intravenous Administration of Antidiphtheritic Serum, *Lancet.,* 20./12, 1902.

Campbell, D.H., Caun, J.R., Friedman, T.R., and Brown, R.A., Reagic Serum Fractions Obtained by Electrophoresis-convention Method. *J. Allergy,* 21:519, 1950.

Carrière, Des Éruptions Consécutives aux Injections de Sérum Antidiphtéritique, *Rev. internat. de med. et de chirurgie,* XIII, 381, 1902.

Castellani, A., Certain Bronchomycoses Which May Simulate Pulmonary Tuberculosis, *J. Trop. Med.,* 32:1,17, 1929.

Celus, A. Cornelius, *Of Medicine,* translated by James Greive, London, 1756.

Coca, A.F., *J. Lab. & Clin. Med.,* 12:1135, 1927.

Coca, A.F., and Grove, E.T., Studies in Hypersensitiveness *J. Immunol.,* 10:445, 1925.

Colley, W., & Egis, B., Die Diphtherie-Epidemien nach dem Material des Morosoff'schen Städtischen Krankenhauses in Moskau in den Jahren 1903-1909, *Jahrb. f. Kinderh. Berl.,* n. F. lxxiii, Ergnzngshft., 27-67, 1911.

Cooke, R.A., Studies in Specific Hypersensitiveness, *J. Immunol.,* 7:119, 1922.

Coons, A.H., Leduc, E.H., and Kaplan, H., Localization of Antigen in Tissue cells, VI: The fate of Infected Foreign Proteins in the Mouse, *J. Exp. Med.,* 93:173, 1951.

Criep, L.H., Mayer, L.D., and Cohen, S.G., Effect of X-radiation on Hypersensitiveness, *J. Allergy,* 21:373, 1950.

Crooke, T.T., Diphtheria: a Review of the Literature for 1923, *Am. J. Dis. Child.* 29:360; 30:367, 1925.

Cushing, H.B., The Story of Diphtheria, *Tr. Canad. Soc. Stud. Dis. Child.,* 4:13-22, 1926.

Czeczowiczka, O., Zur Kenntnis der durch Cytotoxine im Tierkörper Erzeugten Veränderungen, *Ztschft. f. Heilkunde,* 1903.

Czerny, Adalbert, Klienschmidt, Hans, Ueber eine Buttermehlnahrung f. Schwache Säuglinge, *Jahrb. f. Kinderh.,* lxxxvii, 1, 1918.

Dallera, Considerazione e Casi Clinici di Trasfusione del Sangue, *Il Morgagni,* VII, 1874.

Dammin, G.J., and Bukantz, S.C., Modification of Biological Response in Experimental Hypersensitivity, *J.A.M.A.,* 139: 358, 1949.

Detre-Deutsch, Superinfection und Primäraffect, *Wr. Klin. Wo.,* Nr. 27, 1904.

Dewees, Wm. Potts, *A treatise on the physical and medical treatment of children,* Philadelphia, 1825.

Dieulafoy, Chantemess, Widal, Sur une Tuberculose Mycosique, *Verh. X Internat. Med. Congr. Berlin* 1890, Bd. II., Spec Tl, Abt. III, p. 51, 1890.

Efron, B.G., Boatner, C.H., and Dorfman, R.I., *Science,* Preparation of purified house-dust extracts, 91:389, 1940.

Ehrich, W.E., Seifter, J., and Forman, C., Experimental Serum Disease: a Pathogenetic Study, *J. Exp. Med.,* 89:23, 1949.

Ellis, R.V., Rational Grouping of Food Allergens, *J. Allergy,* 2: 246, 1931.

Epstein, Alois, Ueber die Epithelperlen in der Mundhöhle, *Zeitschrift f. Heilkunde I Bd,* Prag, 1880.

Escherich, *Diphtherie, Croup, Serumtherapie,* Wien, Prohaska, 1895.

Escherich, Versuche zur Immunisierung gegen Diphtherie auf dem Wege des Verdauungstractes, *Wr. Klin. Woch.,* 1897.

Escherich, Theodor, *Die Darmbakterien des Saüglings und ihre Beziehungen zur Physiologie der Verdauung,* 1886.

Feinberg, S.M., Seasonal Hay Fever and Asthma due to Molds, *J.A.M.A.*, 107:1861, 1936.

Feldman, William, *Antenatal and Postnatal Child Physiology,* London, 1920.

Fine, J., and A. Seligman, Traumatic Shock, IV: A Study of the Problem of the "Lost Plasma" in the Hemorrhagic Shock by the Use of Radioactive Plasma Protein, *J. Clin. Invest.*, 22: 285, 1943.

Finkelstein, Heinrich, Ueber Alimentare Intoxication im Säuglingsalter, *Jahrb. f. Kinderh.*, lxv, 1, 263, 1907.

Finkelstein, Heinrich and Meyer, L.F., Ueber Eiweissmilch, *Jahrb. f. Kinderh.*, lxxi, 530, 1910.

Fitzgerald, J.G., A Review of Some of the Recent Work on the Diagnosis, Prevention and Treatment of Diphtheria, *Tr. Coll. Physicians Phila.*, 3. ser., 46: 92-128, 1934.

Flood, C.A., Observations on Sensitivity to Dust Fungi in Patients with Asthma, *J.A.MA.*, 96: 2094, 1931.

Foote, John A., Evidence of Rickets prior to 1650, *Am. J. Dis. Child.*, xxiv, 443, 1927.

Francioni, La Malattia da Siero, *Lo Sperimentale*, p. 767, 1904.

Friedenthal und Levandovsky, Über das Verhalten des thierischen Organismus gegen fremdes Blutserum, *Arch. f. Anat. und Physiol.* Bd. 5, 6, p. 531, 1899.

Garrison, Fielding H., *History of Pediatrics—Abt's System of Pediatrics*, W.B. Saunders Co., Phila., i, 1923.

Gautier, P., Quelques Idées Récentes sur la Prophylacie et le Traitment de la Diphtérie, *Rev. méd. Suisse rom.*, 43: 375-86, 1923.

Gerlach, Tod nach Einer Antidiphtherieseruminjektion, *Therap. Monatschefte*, p. 198, April, 1903.

Ghinopoulo, Sophokles, Die Anfänge der Wiener Pädiatrie, *Zeitschr. f. Kinderh.*, xlv, 501, 1928.

Glisson, Francis, Tractatus de Rhachitide sive Morbo Puerili, *Rickets dicto.*, London, 1659.

Haller, P.K., Schwere Erscheinungen mach Injektion des Behringschen Heilserums *Russ.*, p. 151, 1895, *ref. Virchows Jahrb.*, 1895.

Hamburger, F. und Moro, Über die Biologischen Nachweisbaren

Veränderungen des Menschlichen Blutes nach Seruminjektion, *Wr. Klin. Wo.* Nr. 15, 1903.

Hamburger, F., *Arteigenheit und Assimilation*, Wien, Deutike, 1903.

Harrison, W.T. Immunizing value of diphtheria toxinantitoxin mixture and of diphtheria toxoid. *Public Health Reports*, 45: 1883, 1930.

Hasting, C.J., The Evolution of Our Present Knowledge of Diphtheria, *Pub. Health J. Toronto*, 18: 231-34, 1927.

Heidelberger, M., Kendall, F., and Soo Hoo, C.M. Quantitative Studies in the Preciptin Reaction: Antibody Production in Rabbits Injected with an Azo-protein, *J. Exp. Med.*, 58:137, 1933.

Henoch, Edward, *Lectures on Diseases of Children*, 1881.

Herrmann, F., Sulzberger, M.B., and Baer, R.L., Penetration of Allergens into the Human Skin. *New York State J. Med.*, 44:2452, 1944.

Heubner, Praktische Winke zur Behandlung der Diphtherie mit Heilserum, *D. Med. Wo.*, Nr. 36, p. 701, 1894.

Heubner, Otto L., und Rubner, Die Natürliche Ernährung eines Säuglings, *Zeitschr. f. Biologie*, 1898.

Hitchens, A.P., Diphtheria; Epidemiology; Individual Susceptibility and Prophylaxis, with Special Reference to the Schick test; Treatment and Management of Epidemics, *Internat. Clin.*, 32.s., iv. 151-175, i pl., Phila., 1922.

Holmes, Oliver Wendell, The Contagiousness of Puerperal Fever, *New England Quart. Jour. of Med. and Surg.*, i, 503, 1842-43.

Jackson, C., *M. Clin. North America.* 5:637, 1921. Jackson, C., and Jackson, C.L., *Bronchoscopy, Esophogoscopy and Gastroscopy*, Saunders, Philadelphia and London, 1934.

Jacobi, Abraham, *Collectanea*, N.Y., 1909.

Johannessen, Über Injektionem mit Antidiphtherischem Serum und Reinem Pferdeserum, *D. Med. Wo.* Nr. 51, 1895.

Jörgensen, A., "Schwankungen des Agglutinationsvermögens des Blutes im Verlaufe des Typhus abdominalis," *Centrlbl. f. Bact.*, Bd. 38, p. 679, 1905.

Judd, F.H., Diphtheria immunization. *Chinese Med. J.*, 49: 826, 1935.

Kahn, I.S., Urticaria due to food allergy, Texas State J. Med. 27: 14, 1931.

Karelitz, S., Serum sickness, *Ann. N.Y. Acad, Sci.*, 52:705, 1949.

Karlinski, Beeinflusst das Diphtherieheilserum irgendwie den Stoffwechsel im gesundem Organismus?, *Wr. Med. Wo.* Nr. 8, 1895.

Kassowitz, Max, *Praktische Kinderheilkunde*, J. Springer, Berlin, 1910.

Kassowitz, Die Erfolge des Diphtherieheilserums, *Ther. Monatsh.*, 1898.

Kaupe, Ein Fall von Idiosynkrasie gegen Diphtherieheilserum, *Berl. Klin. Wo.* 44, 1899.

Kay, C.F., The Mechanism by which Experimental Nephritis Is Produced in Rabbits Injected with Nephrotoxic Duck Serum, *J. Exp., Med.*, 72:559, 1940.

Kleberger, K., Pneumonomykosis Aspergillina bei Grippe, *Dtsch. med. Wschr.*, 46:1170, 1920.

Kossorotoff, Über die Veränderung des Blutes und Einiger Organe bei Kaninchen nach Subcutaner Injection von Diphtherieheilserum, (*Ref. Jahrb. f. Kdh.*, 1898,)

Kucharzewski, Experimentale Untersuchungen über den Einfluss der Heilsera und des Normalen Pferdeserums auf das Blut, *Wr. medic. Presse*, Nr. 44, 1903.

Lai, D.G., Observations on Diphtheria Immunization with Single Injection of Alum Toxoid. *Chinese Med. J.*, 49:340, 1935.

Landsteiner, K., *The Specificity of Serological Reactions*, Harvard University Press, Cambridge, Mass., 1945.

Latta, H., Gitlin, D., and Janeway, C.A., Experimental Hypersensitivity in the Rabbit: the Cellular Localization of Soluble Azo-proteins (Dye-azo-human Serum Albumins) Injected Intravenously, *Arch. Path.*, 51:260, 1951.

Lawrynowicz, A., Work of Szymon Dzierzgowski on Serology and Epidemiology of Diphtheria, *Polska gaz. lek.*, 8: 153-5, 1929.

Levinson, Abraham, The Pediatric Section of a Medical Cyclopedia of the Seventeenth Century, *Bulletin of the Society of Medical History of Chicago*, ii, 110, Jan. 1919.

Longcope, W.T., and Rackemann, F.M., The Relation of Circulating Antibodies to Serum Disease, *J. Exp. Med.*, 26: 341, 1918.

Longpré, D. Historique de la Diphtérie,*Union méd. Canada*, 62: 365-9, 1933.

Lublinski, Über eine Nachwirkung des Antitoxins bei Behandlung der Diphtherie, *D. Med. Wo.*, Nr. 45, p. 847, 1894.

Malinowski, A., Die Serumbehandlung der Diphtheriekranken, *Gazeta lekarska*, (ref. *Virch. J.B.*), 1895.

Marmorek, *Der Streptokokkus und das Antistreptokokkenserum*, cit. b. Hartung, 1895.

Maxcy, K.F., Some Recent Advances in Diphtheriology, *Am. J.M. Sc.*, 195: 417-25, 1938.

Meigs, Arthur V., *Milk Analysis and Infant Feeding*, P. Blakiston, Son & Co., Phila., 1885.

Meigs, Charles D., *Observations on Certain Diseases of Young Children*, Lea & Blanchard, Phila., 1850.

Meigs, John Forsyth, *A Practical Treatise on the Diseases of Children*, Lindsay and Blakiston, Phila., 1848.

Melnik, Krassnov, Palant and Khorouzenko, *Ann. Inst. Metchnikoff*, Vol. 4, 1936.

Mendelsohn, Ludwig, Erfahrungen über die Behandlung des Scharlachs mit Antistreptokokkenserum, *Deutsche Med. Wochensch.*, p. 461, 1905.

Miller, J.M., and Favour, C.B., The Lymphocytic Origin of a Plasma Factor Responsible for Hypersensitivity in Vitro of a Tuberculin Type, *J. Exp. Med.*, 93:1, 1951.

Moll, F.C., and Hawn, C. v. Z., Experimental Hypersensitivity: a Study in the Relationship of ACTH and Adrenalectomy to the Serological Sequence and Production of Pathological Lesions Following Injection of Heterologous Serum Protein, Abstract, *Am. J. Dis. Child.*, 81:79, 1952.

Moreira De Fonseca, J., Historia de Estudo da Diphteria, *Fol. med. Rio.*, 18: 289-92, 1937.

Moser, P., *Über die Behandlung des Scharlachs mit einem Scharlach-Streptokokkenserum*, Karger, Berlin, 1902.

SELECTED BIBLIOGRAPHY

Moss, William, *An Essay on the Management of Feeding of Infants,* Philadelphia, 1794.

Moyer, A.W., Jervis, G.A., Black, J., Koprowski, H., and Cox, H.R. Action of Adrenocorticotrophic Hormone (ACTH) in Experimental Allergic Encephalomyelitis of the Guinea Pig, *Proc. Soc. Exp. Biol. & Med.,* 75:387, 1950.

Mya, I., Sull' Azione Fisiologica del Siero Antififterico nell Organismo Infantile (Lo Sperimentale, 1895, XLIX, Sezione Clinica fasc. 2.), 1895.

Park, William Hallock, Duration of Immunity Against Diphtheria Achieved by Various Methods, *Journ. of the* A.M.A., 109: 1681, 1937.

Park, W.H., and Zingher, Abraham, Immunity Results Obtained with Diphtheria Toxoid (Modified Toxin) and One-tenth L+Mixtures of Toxin-antitoxin in the Public Schools of New York City. *Am. Journ. of Diseases of Children,* 28: 464, 1924.

Peck, S., and Salomon, G., Eczema of Infancy and Childhood, *Am. J. Dis. Child.,* 46: 1308, 1933.

Peshkin, M.M., and Fineman, A.H., Asthma in Children, *Am. J. Dis. Child.,* 34:815, 1927.

Peshkin, M.M., Dry Pollen Ophthalmic Test in Pollen Asthma and Hay Fever Patients Negative to Cutaneous Tests. *J. Allergy,* 3:20, 1931.

Peshkin, M.M., Critique of Perennial Treatment of Pollen Allergy, *J. Allergy,* 7:477, 1936.

Peshkin, M.M., and Landay, L.H., Cutaneous Reactions to Tobacco Antigen in Allergic and in Nonallergic Children, *Am. J. Dis. Child.,* 57:1288, 1939.

von Pirquet, Clemens, *Congrès international d'Hygiène,* 1903.

von Pirquet, Clemens, Zur Theorie der Vaccination, *Versammlung Deutscher Naturf. und Ärzte.,* Cassel, 1903.

von Pirquet, Clemens, Körpergewichtsbestimmungen bei Nephritis, 76, *Vers. Deutscher Naturf. und Ärzte,* Breslau, 1904.

von Pirquet, Clemens, Zur Frage des Agressins, *Wr. Klin. Wo.,* Nr. 17, 1905.

von Pirquet, Clemens, Allergie Probe zur Diagnose der Tuberkulose im Kindesalter, *Wien. med. Wchnschr.,* xliv, 699, 1907.

von Pirquet, Clemens, and Schick, Béla, *Die Serum Krankheit,* Leipzig, 1905.

von Pirquet and Schick, Zur Theorie der Inkubationszeit, *Wr. Klin. Wo.,* Nr. 26, 45, 1903.

von Pirquet, C., and Schick, B., *Serum Sickness,* Baltimore, 1951.

Pope, C. G., The Production of Toxin by e. Diphtheria, *Brit. J. Exp. Path.,* 13:207, 1932.

Powell, A.T.W., Supply of Measles Antiserum, *Brit. Med. J.,* 1:665, 1936.

Ramon, G., De la Valeur Comparée de l'Anatoxine Diphtérique et du Floculat Anatoxine-antitoxine pour la Production de l'Immunité Antitoxique. Spécifique, *Compt. vend. Soc. de biol.* 98:351, 1928.

Ramon, G., De l'Influence, sur l'Anatoxine Diphtérique, de la Précipitation par Certains Agents Chimiques, *Compt. vend Soc. de biol.* 98:354, 1928.

Rénon, L., *Étude sur l'Aspergillose chez les Animaux et chez l'Homme,* Paris, 1897.

Reuss, Aug. v., *Die Krankheiten des Neugeborenen,* Springer, 1914; *Pathologie der Neugeborenen-Periode,* Pfaundler-Schlossman, i. Aufl., I. Bd., F.C.W. Vogel, Leipzig, 1931.

Rhazes, *Treatise on the smallpox and measles,* trans. by. W.F. Greenhill, London, 1848.

Rich, A.R., The role of Hypersensitivity in Periarteritis Nodesa as Indicated by Seven Cases Developing During Serum Sickness and Sulfanamide Therapy, *Bull. Johns Hopkins Hosp.,* 71:123, 1942.

Rich, A.R., Hypersensitivity in Disease, with Especial Reference to Periarteritis Nodosa, Rheumatic Fever, Disseminated Lupus Erythematosus, and Rheumatoid Arthritis, *Harvey Lectures,* 42:106, 1946-1947.

Rilliet und Barthes, *Traits clinique et pratique des maladies des enfants,* 1853.

Rostoski, Verhandlungen der Physiol. Mediz., *Gesellschaft zu Würzburg,* N.F. Bd. 35.

Rotch, T.M., Essential Principles of Infant Feeding and the

Modern Methods of Applying Them, *J.A.M.A.*, xli, 350, 1903.

Rowe, A.H., *The Elimination Diets and the Patient's Allergy*, Lea & Febiger, Philadelphia, 1944.

Ruhräh, John. *Pediatrics of the Past*, 592 pgs. Paul B. Hoeber, New York, 1925.

Sayers, R.R., and Meriwether, F.V., Lung Disease Due to Unknown Cause, *Am. J. Roetg. & Rad. Ther.*, 27:337, 1932.

Schloss, O., and Weymuller, C. A., Nondiabetic Ketosis in Children, *Am. J. Dis. Child.*, 34:815, 1927.

Schuhardt, V.T., and Cook, E.B.M., Antitoxinogenic value of plain and alum-precipitated toxoid, *Canad. Pub. Health J.*, 27: 278, 1936.

Schütz, Diskussionsbemerkung zu Piorkowski's Vortrage, *Berl. Medic. Gesellsch.*, 7./12, 1904.

Schwab, L., Moll, F.C., Hall, T., Brean. M., Hawn, C. v. Z., and Janeway, C.A., Experimental Hypersensitivity in the Rabbit: Effect of Inhibition of Antibody Formation by X-radiation or Nitrogen Mustards on the Histologic and Serologic Sequences, and on the Behavior of Serum Complement, Following Single Large Injections of Foreign Proteins, *J. Exp. Med.*, 91:505, 1950.

Schwartzman, G., Schneierson, S.S., and Soffer, L.J., Suppression of the Phenomenon of Local Tissue Reactivity by ACTH, Cortisone, and Sodium Salicylate, *Proc. Soc. Exp. Biol. & Med.*, 75:175, 1950.

Seifter, J., Ehrich, W.E., Begany, A.J., and Warren, G.H., Effects of Cortisone, Hyaluronidase, Desoxycorticosterone, and Artisone on Experimental Serum Disease in Rabbits, *Proc. Soc. Exp. Biol. & Med.*, 75:337, 1950.

Selous, D.F., History of Diphtheria, *Brit. M.J.*, 1:355, 1927.

Simon, J.F., *De Lactis Muliebris Ratione Chemica et Physiologica*, Berlin, 1838. Also German translation, *Die Frauenmilch*, Berlin, 1838.

Smith, H.L., Quoted by Brown, A., *J. Immunol.*, 7:97, 1922.

Still, George Frederic. *The History of Paediatrics*, 526 pgs. Oxford University Press, London, 1931.

Storm von Leeuwen, W., Bien, Z., Kremer, W., u. H. Varekamp,

Ueber die Bedeutung Kleinsporiger Aspergillus-Arten (Typus Aspergillus Fumigatus) für die Aetiologie des Asthma Bronchiale, *Ztschr. f. Immunitätsf. u exp. Therapie*, 44:1, 1925.

Super, J. *The Evolution in the Control of Diphtheria*, Wauwatosa, 1936.

Sweany, H.C., Porsche, J.D., and Douglass, J.R., Chemical and Pathologic Study of Pneumonoconiosis with Special Emphasis on Silicosis and Silico-tuberculosis, *Arch. Path.*, 22: 593, 1936.

Thom, Charles, and Church, Margaret B., *The Aspergilli*, Williams & Wilkins Co., Baltimore, 1926.

Thomas, A.M., Report of an Experience with Antitoxin etc., *Med. Record*, 15./6, 1895.

Timmer, Die Serumtherapie bei Diphtherie im Kinderkrankenhause zu Amsterdam, *D. Med. Wo.*, Nr. 37, p. 607, 1895.

Tschistovitch, Étude sur les Propriétés du Sang des Animaux Injectés de Sang ou de Sérum d'une Autre Éspèce Animale, *Arch. Russes de Pathologie*, 1899.

Underwood, Charles, *The Disorders of Childhood*, London, 1797.

Vander Veer, H., et al, *Am. J. M. Sc.*, 174:101, 1927.

Vaughan, W.T., and Black, J.H., *Practice of Allergy*, 2nd ed., C.V. Mosby Co., St. Louis, 1948.

Wahl, E.F., Primary Pulmonary Aspergillosis (Med. Assn. Georgia), *J.A.M.A.*, 91:200, 1928.

Wassermann, A., Über Natürliche und Künstliche Immunität, *Ztschft. f. Hyg.*, Bd. 37, p. 173.

Wassermann, A., und Citron, Die Locale Immunität der Gewebe und Ihre Praktische Wichtigkeit, *D. Med. Wo.*, Nr. 15, p. 573, 1905.

Wedgwood, R.J., Hawn, C. v. Z., and Janeway, C.A., The Mechanism of Action of ACTH in Experimental Nephritis due to Foreign Protein, *Proc. Second Clinical ACTH Conference*, ed. J.R.Mote, 1:108, 1951.

Whytt, Robert, *Observation on the Dropsy of the Brain*, Edinburgh, 1768.

Widal et Rostaine, Pathogénie des Accidents sériques, *Soc. Méd. des Hôpitaux*, séance du 26./5, 1905.

Wlajew, G.M., Experimente an Thieren mit Einfachen und Antidiphth. Pferdeblutserum, *Wratsch*, p. 441, 1895.

Zinsser, H., Hypersensitiveness, *Boston M. & S. J.*, 196:387, 1927.

Index

Abramson, Harold A., 133
Academy of Medicine, The New York, 120, 148
Academy of Medicine Gold Medal, The New York, 148
Addingham Gold Medal, 150
Adler, Alfred, 21
Aetius, 26; on diphtheria, 33
Agressins, About the Question of, 66
Albany, N. Y., 8
Albert Einstein College of Medicine, 178
Allergy, 4, 59; first experiments, 66-71; in United States, 132; hyperergic reaction, 134-137; your friend or enemy, 140-144; forum, 155
Alvares, Arturo, 175
American Academy of Pediatrics on a premature infant, 13
American Pediatric Society, 83, 178
American Relief, 98
Amida, town of, 32
Annales Paediatrici, 147
Ansbach, 51
Arabs, 147
Aretaeus of Cappadocia on tetanus, pneumonia, empyema, abscess of the tonsils, diphtheria and angina, 28
Aristophanes, 94
Arnstein, Leo, 104, 110
Asia, 166
Asphyxia, Trauma, and Shock at Birth, 176
Augustus Caesar, 27

Austria, 5, 6, 46, 61, 76, 97, 101, 104, 147, 148, 152, 154, 182
Austro-Hungarian Army, Medical Division of the, 46, 47, 89, 90
Austro-Hungarian Empire, 10, 18, 47, 57, 88, 94
Avicenna, 27

Baas, Murray H., 159
Bagellardus, Paulus, 28
Balaton Lake, 11, 12, 22, 44
Baltimore, Md., 71
Barcs, town of, 13
Bartlett, Frederick, 128
Basel, 28
Bayla, 3
BCG vaccination, 128-130
Behner, Dorothy, 130
Behring, Emil von, 34, 76, 118
Béla Schick Lecture, 173
Béla Schick Pediatric Department of the Albert Einstein College of Medicine, 178
Bellevue Hospital, 128
Bengal, Province of, 169
Bennington pottery, 162
Berlin (city of), 51, 52, 139
Beth-El Hospital, 174, 177
Bethlehem, 140
Biedert, Philipp, 52
Billard, Charles Michel, 51
Birnberg, L. L., 134
Bliss, Cornelius N., 124
Blumenthal Auditorium, 95, 172
Blumenthal, George, 104